# Science
## 5-6

## Written by
## Marilyn Marks

**Editors:** Carla Hamaguchi and Collene Dobelmann
**Illustrator:** Dimension
**Designer/Production:** Moonhee Pak/Rosa Gandara
**Cover Designer:** Barbara Peterson
**Art Director:** Tom Cochrane
**Project Director:** Carolea Williams

# Table of Contents

# Introduction

Each book in the *Power Practice*™ series contains over 100 ready-to-use activity pages to provide students with skill practice. The fun activities can be used to supplement and enhance what you are already teaching in your classroom. Give an activity page to students as independent class work, or send the pages home as homework to reinforce skills taught in class. An answer key is provided for quick reference.

The practical and creative activities in the science series provide the perfect way to help students develop the science process skills of observing, sorting, classifying, comparing, and analyzing.

*Science 5–6* provides activities that illustrate and explain concepts in life science, earth science, and physical science, and the topics covered correlate with current science standards. Use the reproducible activity pages to enrich students' study of these key topics:
• Human Body
• Plants
• Ecology
• Natural Resources
• Geology
• Weather
• Outer Space
• Chemistry
• Light and Heat

Use these ready-to-go activities to "recharge" skill review and give students the power to succeed!

# Human Skeleton

## HUMAN BODY

> The human skeleton contains over 200 bones. The skeleton gives the body shape and support, and it protects internal organs, such as the brain, heart, and lungs. The bones of your skull have grown together to form a protective covering around your brain. Your rib cage protects your heart and lungs. Strong connective cords, called **ligaments**, hold the bones of the skeleton together.

Match each item to its description.

**1** _____ thigh bone

**2** _____ compact bone

**3** _____ calcium

**4** _____ backbone

**5** _____ cartilage

**6** _____ ligaments

**7** _____ collarbone

**8** _____ shoulder blade

**9** _____ kneecap

**10** _____ spongy bone

**A.** patella

**B.** protects the spinal cord

**C.** cushions the ends of bones

**D.** hard bone tissue found on outer part of bones

**E.** connect bones to other bones

**F.** flexible bone tissue containing collagen

**G.** scapula

**H.** clavicle

**I.** mineral needed for strong, healthy bones

**J.** femur

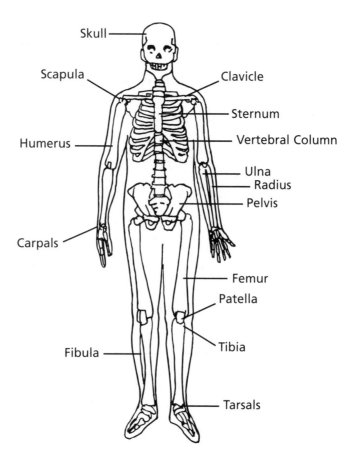

Science • 5–6 © 2005 Creative Teaching Press

Name _____ Date _____

# Types of Joints

### HUMAN BODY

The place where two bones meet is called a **joint**. There are three main types of joints found in the body: immoveable, partially moveable, and freely moveable. **Immoveable joints** have fused together and no longer move. **Partially moveable joints** allow slight movements in all directions. **Freely moveable joints** include pivot joints, hinge joints, ball and socket, and gliding joints.

**Pivot**
Rotates side to side

**Ball and Socket**
Moves all around

**Gliding**
Moves up and down
and side to side

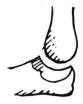
**Hinge Joint**
Bends and straightens

Use the words in the box to complete the sentences. You can use a word more than once.

| neck | hip | wrist | knee | elbow | shoulder | skull | backbone | ankle |

**1** You have immoveable joints in the _____.

**2** Ball and socket joints are found in your _____ and

_____.

**3** Pivot joints are located in your _____ and

_____.

**4** Partially moveable joints are located all along the _____.

**5** Hinge joints are found in your _____ and

_____.

**6** Gliding joints are found in your _____, _____, and

_____.

Science • 5–6 © 2005 Creative Teaching Press

Name _____ Date _____

# The Brain

### HUMAN BODY

The brain is the center of the nervous system. It has three main sections:  the cerebrum, the cerebellum, and the brainstem. The **cerebrum** is the largest section and contains centers for the five senses, pain, memory, reasoning, and speech. The **cerebellum** controls muscular coordination and balance. The small **brainstem** is the most important because it contains the medulla. The **medulla** automatically controls vital life functions, such as your heartbeat, breathing, digestion, and blood pressure.

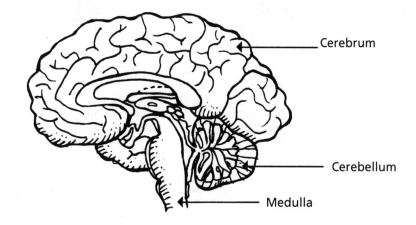

Write **cerebrum**, **cerebellum**, or **medulla** to identify which part of the brain controls the activity.

**1** breathing _____

**2** vision _____

**3** balance _____

**4** heartbeat _____

**5** memory _____

**6** sneezing _____

**7** walking up stairs _____

**8** pain _____

**9** swimming _____

**10** speech _____

Science • 5–6 © 2005 Creative Teaching Press

Name _____  Date _____

# The Nervous System

### HUMAN BODY

The **nervous system** is a complex communications network. The brain is connected to the spinal cord, which branches out into hundreds of nerves. The **nerves** are made of bundles of thin nerve fibers and extend all over the body. **Sensory nerves** receive information from the sense organs and transmit messages to the brain and spinal cord. **Motor nerves** carry responses from the brain and spinal cord out to muscles, organs, and glands.

Dendrite →

Axon

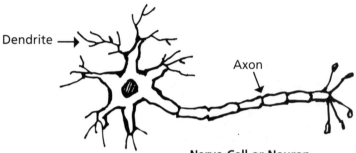

**Nerve Cell or Neuron**

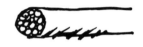

**A Nerve**

Read each statement. Write **T** if the statement is true or **F** if it is false.

**1** _____ Nerve cells, or neurons, carry messages in one direction.

**2** _____ Sensory nerves send messages out to the muscles and glands.

**3** _____ Nerves are made up of bundles of nerve fibers.

**4** _____ The long extension of a nerve cell is called an axon.

**5** _____ Reflex actions occur rapidly because the nerve messages usually only go to the spinal cord.

**6** _____ Nerves branch out from the spinal cord and extend all over the body.

**7** _____ Motor nerves receive messages from your sense organs.

**8** _____ Nerve fibers are very thin.

**9** _____ Nerve impulses travel very fast.

**10** _____ Dendrites receive nerve impulses and send them to the cell body of the neuron.

Name _____ Date _____

# The Heart

### Human Body

The **heart** is a small but amazing muscular pump. The upper chambers receive blood and send it to the lower chambers. Then the blood is pumped into the arteries, which carry it all over the body. There are valves between the chambers that keep the blood from flowing backwards. Other valves are located at the openings of arteries that leave the heart. The closing of the valves causes the sound of your heartbeat.

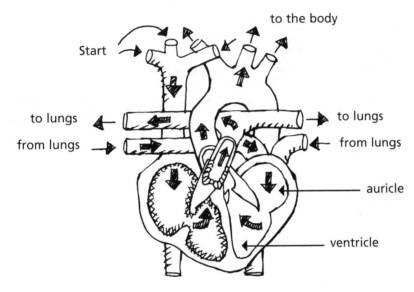

| valves |
| ventricles |
| auricles |
| lungs |
| body |
| pump |
| receive |
| blood |

Use the words in the box to complete the sentences.

**1** The heart continuously pumps _____ all throughout the body.

**2** The sound of your heartbeat is made by the closing of _____ within the heart.

**3** The right side of your heart sends blood to the _____.

**4** The left side of your heart sends blood to the _____.

**5** The lower chambers of the heart, called _____, have thick, muscular walls.

**6** The upper chambers _____ the blood flowing into the heart.

**7** The job of the ventricles is to _____ the blood out of the heart.

**8** The upper chambers are called _____.

Name _____ Date _____

# Your Blood

### HUMAN BODY

Your blood travels away from the heart in **arteries,** and it flows back towards the heart in **veins.** Arteries and veins branch into smaller vessels that finally reach the tiny capillaries. **Capillaries** connect arteries to veins. **Plasma** is the liquid part of the blood, and it carries nutrients to all the cells. Within the blood are red blood cells, white blood cells, and platelets. The blood helps to maintain the body's temperature.

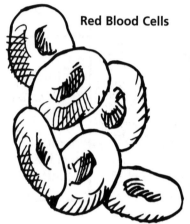

**Red Blood Cells**

 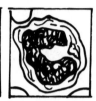   

**White Blood Cells**

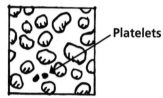 — **Platelets**

Read each statement. Write **T** if the statement is true or **F** if it is false.

**1** _____ The blood platelets help to stop bleeding and form a blood clot.

**2** _____ The white blood cells carry oxygen to the cells of the body.

**3** _____ The plasma carries digested food nutrients and hormones in the blood.

**4** _____ Red blood cells carry away carbon dioxide waste from the cells.

**5** _____ White blood cells fight off disease by killing germs.

**6** _____ The blood flows back to the heart in arteries.

**7** _____ Capillaries are the tiniest blood vessels.

**8** _____ There are more white blood cells in the blood than red blood cells.

**9** _____ The blood helps to maintain the body's temperature.

**10** _____ Plasma is made mostly of water.

Name _____ Date _____

# What Are Carbohydrates and Fats?

### HUMAN BODY

Carbohydrates and fats supply the body with energy. **Carbohydrates** are compounds made of sugars and starches. Each gram of carbohydrate produces 4 calories in your body. However, every gram of fat produces 9 calories. Your body can store extra fat until you need more energy. Some fats are also used to help build new cells in the body.

**Sources of Carbohydrates**

**Sources of Fats**

Write **C** on the line if the sentence describes carbohydrates. Write **F** if the sentence describes fats.

**1** _____ Used as the body's main source of energy.

**2** _____ Are made of sugars and starches.

**3** _____ Provide 9 calories for every gram eaten.

**4** _____ Our main source is from eating plants.

**5** _____ Are needed in small amounts to help build new cells.

**6** _____ We get them from eating animal products and some plants.

**7** _____ Each gram produces 4 calories in your body.

**8** _____ A layer under the skin provides insulation and helps to keep us warm.

Science • 5–6 © 2005 Creative Teaching Press

Name _____ Date _____

# What Are Proteins?

## Human Body

**Proteins** are chemical compounds that repair damaged cells and help to build new ones. Your hair and fingernails are almost entirely protein. Muscles need proteins to work properly. The body could not function without proteins as they are a part of every cell. Long chains of building blocks, called **amino acids**, form many different kinds of proteins.

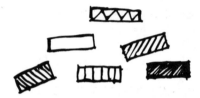

**Amino Acids**

**Proteins**

Put a ✓ by the sentences that describe proteins.

**1** _____ They are our main source of energy in the body.

**2** _____ They repair damaged cells.

**3** _____ Muscles need them in order to function.

**4** _____ They are essential ingredients in every cell.

**5** _____ We can get them from plant and animal sources.

**6** _____ They are built by linking sugar molecules together.

**7** _____ Your hair contains a lot of protein.

**8** _____ Long chains of amino acids form proteins.

Science • 5–6 © 2005 Creative Teaching Press

Name _____ Date _____

# Digestion

HUMAN BODY

Digestion breaks down the food that we eat into a simpler form that our cells can use. This process begins in the mouth, continues in the stomach, and is finally finished in the small intestine. The liver and the pancreas make special digestive juices that aid in the breakdown of food in the small intestine. Extra water and any leftover nutrients are absorbed in the large intestine before wastes are removed from the body.

Number the sentences from 1 to 6 to show the order of how food is digested in the body.

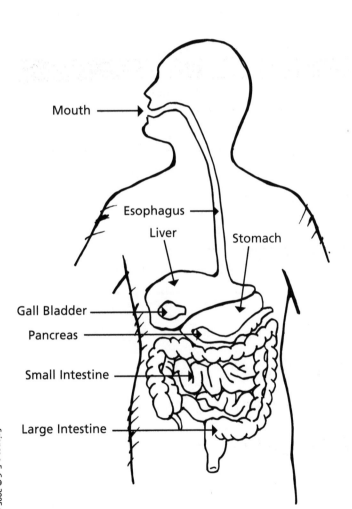

_____ Saliva in the mouth mixes with the food; carbohydrate digestion begins.

_____ The liver and pancreas send digestive juices to the small intestine.

_____ Food passes down the esophagus to the stomach; protein digestion begins.

_____ Digested food is absorbed into the bloodstream in the small intestine.

_____ The small intestine finishes digesting carbohydrates and proteins; fats are now completely digested.

_____ The large intestine absorbs extra water; solid wastes are ready for removal from the body.

Name _____ Date _____

# Vitamins

HUMAN BODY

Vitamins are essential compounds that help the body to grow and function normally. With the exception of some vitamin D, the body cannot manufacture vitamins. Therefore, we need to eat foods that contain these vitamins. We only need small amounts of various vitamins in order to stay healthy. However, you can become sick if you do not eat foods that contain essential vitamins.

| Vitamin | Body Use | Food Source |
|---|---|---|
| A | Maintains healthy skin and eyesight | Milk, eggs, yellow and green vegetables |
| $B_1$ | Promotes healthy nervous system | Milk, meat, cereals, green vegetables |
| $B_2$ | Promotes smooth, healthy skin | Milk, green and leafy vegetables |
| B complex | Aids in metabolism of food | Meat, vegetables, fruit, cereals |
| C | Promotes healthy teeth and gums; aids in healing | Citrus fruits, green vegetables |
| D | Maintains strong bones and teeth | Milk, eggs, liver |
| K | Helps blood to clot | Tomatoes, green vegetables |

Use the chart to answer the questions.

**1** We can obtain many of the vitamins we need by drinking _____.

**2** Vitamin _____ helps stop the bleeding when you cut your finger.

**3** Our bodies can manufacture some vitamin _____ after exposure to sunlight.

**4** Citrus fruits are very rich in vitamin _____.

**5** You will see better at night if you eat foods that have vitamin _____.

**6** Vitamin _____ is important for having smooth, healthy skin.

Name _____ Date _____

# Minerals We Eat

## HUMAN BODY

**Minerals** are inorganic compounds that are needed for healthy growth and the repair of the body. **Calcium** is important for strong muscles, bones, and teeth. **Iron** helps red blood cells carry oxygen. **Magnesium** helps your nerves to send impulses better. **Potassium** helps muscles and nerves function and plays a role in the regulation of blood pressure. **Phosphorus** is important in the release of energy from food.

Potassium

Iron

Phosphorus

Magnesium

Calcium

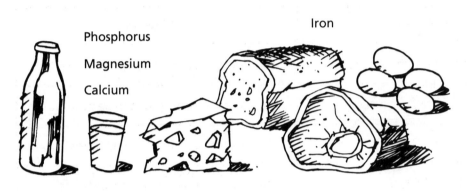

Match each item to its description.

**1** _____ calcium

**2** _____ iron

**3** _____ potassium

**4** _____ magnesium

**5** _____ phosphorus

**6** _____ milk

**7** _____ bananas and apples

**8** _____ meat, bread, and eggs

**A.** foods that supply potassium

**B.** mineral that helps red blood cells carry oxygen

**C.** food that supplies calcium, magnesium, and phosphorus

**D.** mineral that helps nerves send impulses

**E.** mineral needed for strong bones and teeth

**F.** foods that supply iron

**G.** mineral that helps regulate blood pressure

**H.** mineral that helps release energy from food

Name _____  Date _____

# A Balanced Diet

HUMAN BODY

If you follow the recommendations of the food pyramid, you will supply your body with the right amounts of proteins, carbohydrates, fats, vitamins, and minerals. Try to eat servings from the bread, fruit, vegetable, meat, and dairy group at most meals. The expression "junk food" refers to food that has very little, if any, nutritional value. Junk food is mostly empty calories from lots of refined sugar or extra fat.

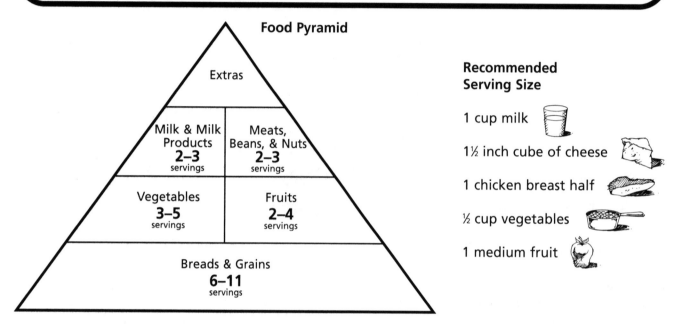

**Food Pyramid**

Extras

Milk & Milk Products
**2–3** servings

Meats, Beans, & Nuts
**2–3** servings

Vegetables
**3–5** servings

Fruits
**2–4** servings

Breads & Grains
**6–11** servings

**Recommended Serving Size**

1 cup milk

1½ inch cube of cheese

1 chicken breast half

½ cup vegetables

1 medium fruit

Write the name of the food group that is needed to balance each meal.

**1** _____  Hamburger on a bun with lettuce and tomato, low-fat milk, and two cookies

**2** _____  Spaghetti topped with tomato sauce and cheese, carrot sticks, and fruit juice

**3** _____  Stir-fried vegetables with chicken, rice, grapes, and water

Circle the items that should be eaten sparingly because they do not provide much, if any, nutrition.

| | | | | |
|---|---|---|---|---|
| Candy | Pretzels | Apple | Soda | Donut |
| Crackers | Jelly | Catsup | Ice Cream | Raisins |
| Fruit Roll | Plain Popcorn | Fruit Juice | Watermelon | Chips |

# Your Lungs

### HUMAN BODY

Your lungs, trachea, bronchial tubes, and diaphragm make up the respiratory system. They all work together to bring oxygen into the body and remove carbon dioxide waste. Your lungs are not two big bags, but they are like large clusters of grapes. Each lung is made of many tiny air sacs, called **alveoli**. After the lungs absorb oxygen, the blood carries it to all the cells in your body.

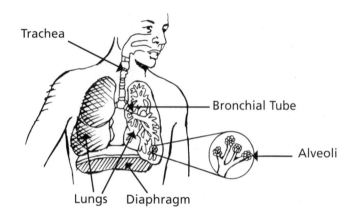

Trachea

Bronchial Tube

Alveoli

Lungs    Diaphragm

Read each statement. Write **T** if the statement is true or **F** if it is false.

**1** _____ We inhale because the air pressure inside the chest cavity is less than outside the body.

**2** _____ The lungs are composed of hundreds of tiny air sacs, called alveoli.

**3** _____ Air enters through the nose or mouth and passes into the trachea.

**4** _____ The diaphragm moves upward during inhalation.

**5** _____ The muscles attached to the ribs make the chest cavity enlarge when we inhale.

**6** _____ Oxygen is absorbed into the bloodstream in the trachea.

**7** _____ The bronchial tubes branch off from the trachea like an upside-down letter Y.

**8** _____ We exhale to remove excess oxygen from the lungs.

**9** _____ The rib cage moves in and down when we exhale.

**10** _____ We exhale because the air pressure inside the chest cavity is greater than outside the body.

# The Excretory System

## HUMAN BODY

The **excretory system** removes wastes from the body. The lungs remove carbon dioxide. The large intestine removes solid wastes. The kidneys remove liquid wastes. The kidneys filter and clean the blood to remove unneeded minerals and leftovers from protein digestion. Extra water is added to this mixture to make urine. The urine is stored in the urinary bladder until it is removed from the body.

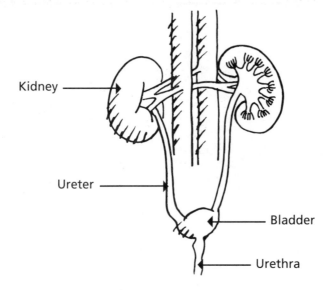

Kidney

Ureter

Bladder

Urethra

Use the words in the box to complete the sentences.

| kidney | ureter | urethra | minerals | protein | bladder | water |
|--------|--------|---------|----------|---------|---------|-------|

**1** The main organ of the excretory system is the _____, which removes liquid wastes.

**2** Urine is stored in the _____ until it is removed from the body.

**3** The _____ is a tube that leads from the kidney to the bladder.

**4** Tiny tubes in the kidney filter the blood to remove unneeded _____.

**5** The kidneys also remove the leftovers from _____ digestion, which are harmful if not removed from the body.

**6** Urine leaves the body through a thin tube called the _____.

**7** Urine is mostly made of _____.

Science • 5–6 © 2005 Creative Teaching Press

Name _____ Date _____

# Muscles at Work

HUMAN BODY

There are three types of muscle tissue in your body. **Cardiac muscle** is found only in the heart and works all the time. **Smooth muscle** is found throughout the digestive tract and in other internal organs. Your brain automatically controls both cardiac and smooth muscle. The only muscles you have conscious control over are the **skeletal muscles**. They are found all over your skeleton and are attached to the bones by tendons.

**Skeletal Muscle**

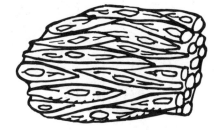

**Smooth Muscle**

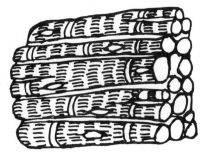

**Cardiac Muscle**

Write **skeletal**, **smooth**, or **cardiac** to identify the main type of muscle tissue that performs each function.

**1** _____ Climbing a flight of stairs

**2** _____ Blinking when an insect flies close to your face

**3** _____ Making your heart beat regularly

**4** _____ Sneezing when dust tickles your nose

**5** _____ Pushing the food through the digestive tract

**6** _____ Squeezing the walls of arteries to help pump blood in the body

**7** _____ Lifting a heavy box and carrying it across a room

**8** _____ Chewing your food at lunch

**9** _____ Talking in class without permission

Name _____ Date _____

# The Skin

### HUMAN BODY

The skin is one of the largest organs in the body. It is your first line of defense because it keeps dirt and germs out of the body. It is important to wash a cut because dirt and germs can enter through an opening in the skin. Your skin has oil glands that help keep the skin soft, sweat glands for cooling, nerves for feeling, and blood vessels that bring nourishment and oxygen to the cells.

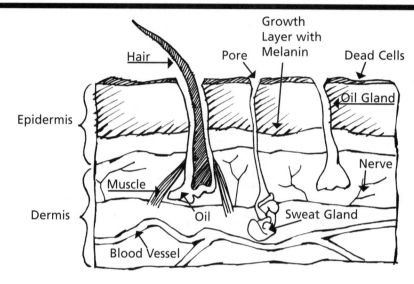

Match each item to its description.

**1** _____ oil glands

**2** _____ sweat glands

**3** _____ pores

**4** _____ dermis

**5** _____ melanin

**6** _____ epidermis

**7** _____ nerves

**8** _____ tiny muscles

**A.** openings in skin that let the sweat out; if clogged with dirt and oil pimples form

**B.** cause movement of hair and skin; cause goose bumps

**C.** keep skin soft and make hair shiny

**D.** gives skin its color; moves to the surface after exposure to sun

**E.** let your skin feel heat, cold, pain, pressure, and touch

**F.** upper layer of skin; where new cells grow

**G.** help to cool the body

**H.** lower layer of skin; contains main blood vessels

Science • 5–6 © 2005 Creative Teaching Press

# Human Body Crossword Puzzle

### HUMAN BODY

Write the word that best matches each clue to complete the crossword puzzle. Use the words in the box for help.

| liver | organ | teeth | tissue | heart | bones | kidney |
|-------|-------|-------|--------|-------|-------|--------|
| muscles | esophagus | lungs | intestines | ligaments | tendon | |

**Across**

1. skinny tube that connects the throat to the stomach
3. large, reddish-brown organ that helps digest fatty foods
4. strong fibers that connect bones to bones
5. bean-shaped organ that removes liquid wastes
7. strong fiber that connects muscles to bones
8. a group of cells working together
10. what our skeleton is made of
11. organ that pumps blood through the body

**Down**

2. organs that we breathe with
6. these make us move
7. what we use to chew with
9. a group of tissues working together
12. where most of digestion takes place

# Contagious Diseases

### Human Body

Sometimes you get sick if you are exposed to germs (bacteria or a virus) in the air, in the water, or in food you eat. Other times you can get sick if you touch someone else who is sick. Illnesses and diseases that can be "caught" are called **contagious diseases.** The bacteria or virus gets into your bloodstream and begins to reproduce. When you have a fever, it is a sign that the body is trying to fight the illness.

| Disease or Illness | Caused By | Method of Transmission |
|---|---|---|
| Common Cold and Flu | Virus | Through the air and contact |
| Measles | Virus | Through the air and contact |
| Chicken Pox | Virus | Through the air and contact |
| Pneumonia | Bacteria | Through the air |
| Food Poisoning | Bacteria | Through food and water |

Read each statement. Write **T** if the statement is true or **F** if it is false.

**1** _____ Washing your hands before eating can help prevent the transmission of germs.

**2** _____ Vaccines are available that prevent the common cold.

**3** _____ Many germs are transmitted through the air when people cough or sneeze.

**4** _____ Bacteria cause most of the common childhood diseases.

**5** _____ You should not share eating utensils with someone who has a contagious disease.

**6** _____ You usually get sick from a contagious disease the same day of exposure to the germs.

**7** _____ It is best to stay home from school when you have a contagious disease.

**8** _____ A fever indicates that your body is trying to fight off disease germs.

**9** _____ It is important to get plenty of rest and drink fluids when you are sick.

Science • 5–6 © 2005 Creative Teaching Press

Name _____ Date _____

# Noncontagious Diseases

### Human Body

A **noncontagious illness** or disease is one that you cannot catch from someone else. Sometimes the condition is inherited from your parents. Other times you develop it on your own. Common allergies, ear infections, diabetes, and asthma are examples of noncontagious diseases. Most noncontagious diseases are controlled with medication that a doctor prescribes.

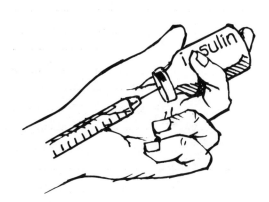

**Insulin helps people with diabetes.**

**Inhalers help people with asthma.**

Put a ✓ by the sentences that describe noncontagious diseases.

**1** _____ You cannot catch diabetes from someone.

**2** _____ People who have asthma often carry an inhaler with them in case of an asthma attack.

**3** _____ You will always get more ear infections if you go swimming.

**4** _____ People with hay fever allergies are sensitive to dust and pollen in the air.

**5** _____ You can sometimes outgrow a food allergy when you become an adult.

**6** _____ Some noncontagious illnesses are inherited from our parents.

**7** _____ There are vaccines that can prevent many noncontagious diseases.

**8** _____ Most noncontagious illnesses and diseases are controlled with medication.

**9** _____ You should avoid touching someone with diabetes or asthma.

Name _____ Date _____

# Seed Plants

PLANTS

Most of the plants you are familiar with produce seeds. Seed plants are divided into two groups: gymnosperms and angiosperms. **Gymnosperms** are also called conifers because their seeds are formed in a cone. Most gymnosperms are trees. **Angiosperms** produce flowers that form some type of fruit with seeds. This group includes all garden flowers, weeds, grasses, cereal grains, and many trees and shrubs.

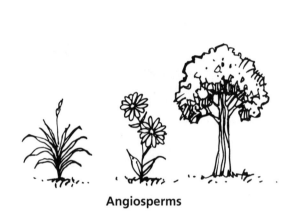

**Angiosperms**

**Gymnosperms**

Write **A** if the sentence describes angiosperms, **G** if it describes gymnosperms, or **B** if it describes both types of plants.

**1** _____ This group includes most of the plants in the world.

**2** _____ These plants have special tubes, known as vascular tissue, for carrying food and water.

**3** _____ These plants have exposed seeds that are produced in cones.

**4** _____ These plants produce flowers that make the seeds.

**5** _____ Several of these plants are trees.

**6** _____ These plants are also known as conifers.

**7** _____ The rose, lemon tree, ivy, and wheat belong to this group.

**8** _____ The pine, fir, cedar, and spruce belong to this group.

**9** _____ These plants have well-developed roots, stems, and leaves.

Name _____ Date _____

# Flowering Plants

PLANTS

Flowering plants, or angiosperms, are the most varied division in the plant kingdom. There are woody plants, such as trees, shrubs, and vines, as well as soft-stemmed plants like grasses and garden flowers. Flowering plants have broad, flat leaves. Many of these plants lose their leaves in the winter. Angiosperms are subdivided into monocots and dicots, based on the number of seed leaves the plant produces.

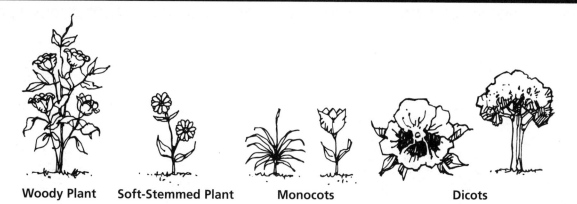

**Woody Plant**   **Soft-Stemmed Plant**   **Monocots**   **Dicots**

Use the words in the box to complete the sentences.

| woody | deciduous | soft-stemmed | monocots | dicots | fibrous | tap |

**1** Plants that lose their leaves in the winter are called _____ plants.

**2** Plants with _____ roots have many roots of a similar size.

**3** Plants with _____ roots have one large root, with much smaller roots growing from it.

**4** Plants with a _____ stem are strong, and this hard stem continues to grow year after year.

**5** _____ plants are more delicate and usually only live for a year or two.

**6** _____ have one seed leaf, and include the lily, tulip, grasses, and cereal grains.

**7** _____ have two seed leaves, and include vegetables, flowering trees, and pansies.

Science • 5–6 © 2005 Creative Teaching Press

# Pollination and Fertilization

PLANTS

Flowering plants reproduce by the processes of pollination and fertilization. During pollination, pollen grains are transferred from the stamens to the female part of a flower, called the **pistil.** A pollen grain grows a tube down to the ovary. During fertilization, sperm cells within the pollen grain swim down to the ovary and unite with an egg inside. Fertilization starts the development of a seed.

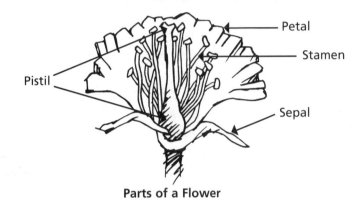

**Parts of a Flower**

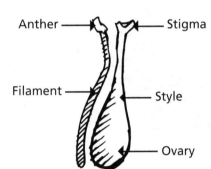

**Stamen and Pistil Close-up View**

Read each statement. Write **T** if the statement is true or **F** if it is false.

**1** _____ The transfer of pollen from the anther to stigma of the same flower is called cross-pollination.

**2** _____ Pollen is often carried from one plant to another plant by the wind, water, or insects.

**3** _____ The male part of the flower is called the stamen.

**4** _____ In order for seeds to develop, the pollen must fall on the pistil of the same type of plant.

**5** _____ Self-pollination is the most common way that flowering plants reproduce.

**6** _____ The female part of the flower is called the pistil.

**7** _____ Pollen grains are formed within the stigma.

**8** _____ Flowers always have one pistil and four stamens.

**9** _____ Sepals protect the flower bud before it opens.

**10** _____ Flower petals are usually brightly colored, which helps to attract insects.

Name _____ Date _____

# Conifers

PLANTS

Conifers belong to the division of plants called **gymnosperms.** They are also called **evergreens** because most conifers keep green leaves all year long. The leaves may last from two to five years. The leaves of these plants are thin and needle-like or resemble small, overlapping scales. Conifers have a sticky, resinous sap not found in angiosperm trees. Most conifers make male and female cones.

**Pine**          **Spruce**

**Male Cone**

**Female Cone**

Put a ✓ next to the sentences that describe conifers.

**1** _____ Conifers are also known as evergreens.

**2** _____ Conifers have big, broad, flat leaves.

**3** _____ The wood of these trees is commonly used for construction lumber and for paper products.

**4** _____ Conifers produce a sticky, resinous sap.

**5** _____ Many conifer trees are used as Christmas trees.

**6** _____ Conifers produce their seeds inside flowers.

**7** _____ Most conifers produce separate male and female cones.

**8** _____ The leaves of conifers can last from two to five years.

**9** _____ The wood of these trees is most often used for making furniture.

**10** _____ These trees do not grow well in areas where it snows a lot.

Name _____ Date _____

# Photosynthesis

PLANTS

Green plants can manufacture their own food using carbon dioxide from the air, water, and energy from sunlight. The **chlorophyll** in a plant is able to trap the sun's energy to aid in the breakdown of water into hydrogen and oxygen. Carbon dioxide combines with the released hydrogen to create simple sugar, usually glucose. The extra oxygen is released back into the air. The sugar can be converted into starch for storage.

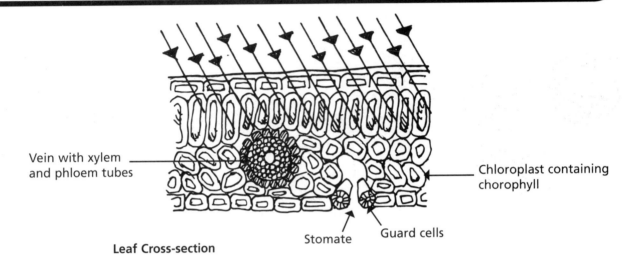

Vein with xylem and phloem tubes

Chloroplast containing chorophyll

Stomate    Guard cells

**Leaf Cross-section**

Read each statement. Write **T** if the statement is true or **F** if it is false.

**1** _____ Guard cells control the opening and closing of the stomates.

**2** _____ Chlorophyll is the green pigment found in plants.

**3** _____ Oxygen is needed for photosynthesis to take place.

**4** _____ The food made during photosynthesis is simple sugar.

**5** _____ The woody stems and branches of plants carry on photosynthesis, too.

**6** _____ Carbon dioxide enters the plant through the roots.

**7** _____ Xylem tubes carry the water through the plant.

**8** _____ Phloem tubes carry the food through the plant.

**9** _____ Chlorophyll traps the energy of the sun.

**10** _____ Oxygen is a waste product of photosynthesis.

Science • 5–6 © 2005 Creative Teaching Press

Name _____ Date _____

# How Plants Package Seeds

PLANTS

Gymnosperms package their seeds in cones. Angiosperms show a lot more variety. A **fruit** is the ripened ovary of a developed flower. The fruit contains the seeds. Some plants make one large seed, while others have many smaller seeds. Seeds may grow in pods or soft, fleshy fruits. Nuts and grains form inside a dry, hard covering. Some plants, like the strawberry, have their seeds on the outside of the fruit.

Write the name of each fruit under the proper heading to show how its seeds are packaged.

| | | | | |
|---|---|---|---|---|
| wheat | apple | orange | green peas | string beans |
| tomato | watermelon | soybeans | pecan | black-eyed peas |
| sunflower | oats | cucumber | acorn | pinto beans |

**Seed Pods**          **Fleshy Fruits**          **Dry Fruits**

_____     _____     _____

_____     _____     _____

_____     _____     _____

_____     _____     _____

Name _____ Date _____

# Plant Word Scramble

Unscramble the words and complete the definitions.

**1** SINYTOPHOSTHES _____: the process by which green plants manufacture food

**2** SMREPSAONIG _____: the name for flowering plants

**3** AENTSM _____: the name of the male part of a flower

**4** SYOSPGMNEMR _____: the name for nonflowering seed plants

**5** PLIITS _____: the name of the female part of a flower

**6** EGYOXN is _____: a waste product of photosynthesis

**7** LYRCOPHHLOL _____: the green pigment in green plants

**8** PONOITANLLI _____: the process needed to fertilize a flower

**9** NCROEFI _____: another name for evergreens

**10** SELVAE _____: the part of the plant where most photosynthesis occurs

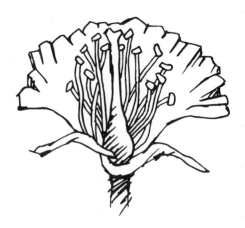

Name _____  Date _____

# Ferns and Mosses

### PLANTS

> **Mosses** are very primitive plants without any tubes for carrying food or water. They are small plants that always live where it is very moist. **Ferns** have vascular tissue (xylem and phloem tubes), and thus can grow larger. Ferns vary in size from small plants up to the size of small trees. The compound leaves of fern plants are called **fronds**. Ferns and mosses do not make seeds. They produce spores to help them reproduce.

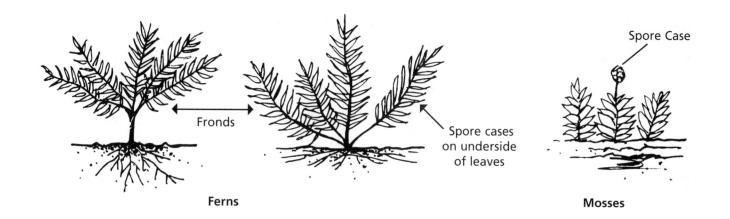

Fronds

Spore cases on underside of leaves

Spore Case

**Ferns**

**Mosses**

Write **M** if the sentence describes mosses, **F** if it describes ferns, or **B** if it describes both ferns and mosses.

**1** _____ These plants do not make seeds.

**2** _____ These plants grow as small, velvety clusters in moist areas.

**3** _____ These plants can grow to be the size of small trees.

**4** _____ These plants reproduce with spores.

**5** _____ These plants have no vascular tissue for carrying food and water.

**6** _____ Spore cases form on the underside of the leaves.

**7** _____ These plants are often used in the garden and as decorative indoor plants.

**8** _____ These plants are used to line hanging flower baskets because they absorb a lot of water.

Name _____  Date _____

# Algae

PLANTS

**Algae** are sometimes a mystery to scientists who try to decide whether or not they fit in our classification system as plants. Many algae are tiny, one-celled organisms that live in fresh water and salt water. Others grow in thin filaments, and some form a giant mass of seaweeds. Millions of microscopic algae living in the ocean give the water a greenish color. Algae contain chlorophyll and can carry on photosynthesis.

**Green Algae**          **Giant Kelp**          **Microscopic Algae**          **Sea Palm**

Use the words in the box to complete the sentences.

| plants | microscopic | seaweed | kelp | chlorophyll | food | scum |

**1** Algae are primitive organisms that contain _____.

**2** Scientists do not classify all types of algae as _____.

**3** Most algae are so small they are _____.

**4** Several larger types of algae that grow in the ocean are commonly called _____.

**5** Giant _____ is one of the largest algae, reaching lengths up to 70 meters (76.6 yd).

**6** Algae growing in lakes and ponds often look like green _____ on the water's surface.

**7** Algae are an important source of _____ for small aquatic and marine animals.

Science • 5–6 © 2005 Creative Teaching Press

# Ecosystems

### ECOLOGY

An **ecosystem** includes the living communities and the nonliving parts of the environment. All the plants, animals, and microscopic organisms compose the living communities. The temperature, rainfall, humidity, sunlight, air quality, and soil composition are the nonliving parts of the environment. Any one of these environmental factors can limit or determine what plants or animals can survive in an ecosystem.

What would limit the survival of each of the following? Write **S** if it is the amount of sunlight, **T** if it is the temperature, **R** if it is the amount of rainfall, or **C** if it is the composition of the soil.

**1** _____ The formation of deserts

**2** _____ The process of photosynthesis

**3** _____ The adaptation of animals to hibernate

**4** _____ Many plants that eat insects live in nitrogen-poor, acidic soil

**5** _____ Ferns are adapted to living in the shade

**6** _____ The rate of transpiration for plants

# Nature's Decomposers

ECOLOGY

The **decomposers** in the environment cause dead plants and animals to decay. They break down complex compounds and return simpler, useful nutrients to the soil. Many decomposers, like bacteria, are microscopic. Others, such as molds and fungi, are large enough to be seen with the naked eye. Decomposers are vital to recycling nitrogen and carbon in the environment.

Put a ✓ by the sentences that describe the effects of decomposers.

**1** \_\_\_\_\_ A dead tree gradually begins to crumble and fall apart.

**2** \_\_\_\_\_ Vultures eat the meat of dead animals.

**3** \_\_\_\_\_ Earthworms loosen the soil as they crawl through it.

**4** \_\_\_\_\_ Many bacteria cause dead animals to rot.

**5** \_\_\_\_\_ We find skeletons of animals many years after their death.

**6** \_\_\_\_\_ Simple carbon and nitrogen compounds are returned to the soil.

**7** \_\_\_\_\_ Humus helps to enrich the soil.

**8** \_\_\_\_\_ Minerals dissolved in water help to form petrified wood.

Name _____ Date _____

# Habitat vs. Niche

A **habitat** is the place where an organism lives within an ecosystem. For example, parrots live in the canopy layer of a tropical rain forest. That is their habitat. The word **niche** describes the position, or role, of the organism within its community. It tells us if the plant or animal is a producer, primary consumer, secondary consumer, tertiary consumer, or decomposer. Parrots are primary consumers (herbivores).

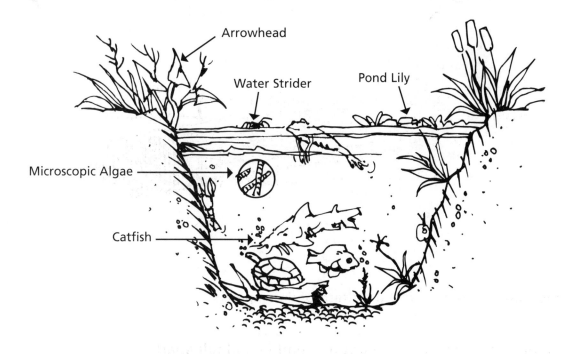

Read each statement. Write **T** if the statement is true or **F** if it is false.

**1** _____ The frog's habitat is near the surface of the pond.

**2** _____ The frog's niche is a secondary consumer (carnivore).

**3** _____ Microscopic algae are primary consumers in the pond.

**4** _____ Cattails, arrowhead, and pond lilies are producers in the pond.

**5** _____ The catfish's habitat is nearer the bottom of the pond.

**6** _____ The fish and turtles are consumers in the pond.

**7** _____ The water strider's habitat is at the middle depths of the pond.

Name _____ Date _____

# Food Webs

### ECOLOGY

> The transfer of energy from producers to consumers to decomposers makes a **food chain**. Within an ecosystem there will be many overlapping food chains. A few producers may become food for several different primary consumers. Likewise, the secondary consumers may compete for their food source. These interlocking **food webs** help to create a balance in nature.

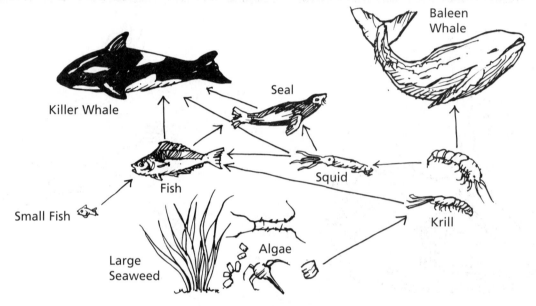

Use the words from the box to complete the sentences.

| producers | predators | seals | killer whales | baleen whales | bacteria | squid |
|---|---|---|---|---|---|---|

**1** Larger animals are known as consumers, or _____, because they prey on smaller animals.

**2** All of the possible food chains that could be formed from the examples above would end with _____, which are the decomposers.

**3** The microscopic algae and larger seaweeds are the _____ in several food chains.

**4** The algae are eaten by the krill, which are eaten by squid, which are eaten by _____, which are eaten by _____.

**5** _____ as well as _____ enjoy a favorite meal of krill.

Science • 5–6 © 2005 Creative Teaching Press

Name _____ Date _____

# Harmful Symbiotic Relationships

### ECOLOGY

When two different types of organisms live together it is called **symbiosis.** This interaction can be neutral, helpful, or harmful. The most common harmful type of relationship is parasitism. **Parasitism** is when one organism lives in or on another organism and harms it to some degree. The animal that is being harmed is called the **host.** There are many different types of parasites in every community and ecosystem.

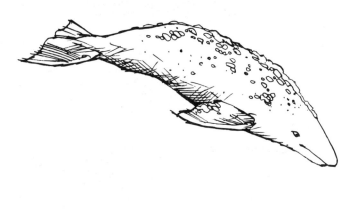

Put a ✓ by all the sentences that are examples of harmful, parasitic relationships.

**1** _____ Fleas and ticks live on dogs and receive nourishment from their host's blood.

**2** _____ Barnacles can attach themselves on the back of crab shells.

**3** _____ Tapeworms live in the intestines of many animals, absorbing the food the larger animals eat.

**4** _____ Many whales have whale lice living on their skin.

**5** _____ Leaf miner insects burrow tunnels inside the leaves of plants.

**6** _____ Cows, chickens, and goats can live together on a farm.

**7** _____ Hawks hunt and kill mice to eat.

**8** _____ Chestnut fungus infected the bark of American chestnut trees and destroyed thousands of them.

Science • 5–6 © 2005 Creative Teaching Press

Name _____ Date _____

# Helpful Symbiotic Relationships

ECOLOGY

Fortunately, there are many examples of helpful relationships between animals, or even between animals and plants. These relationships are a form of symbiosis. **Commensalism** is a relationship where one partner benefits but the other is not affected. When both partners benefit from the relationship it is called **mutualism**. Nature provides us with many examples of unusual partnerships.

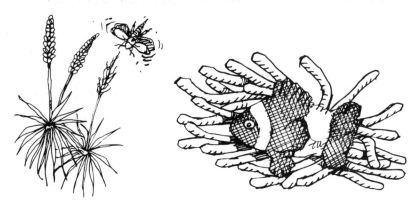

Use the words in the box to complete the sentences.

| sea anemone | cleaner fish | cactus | lichen | sea slugs | protozoa | moth |
|---|---|---|---|---|---|---|

**1** A _____ lives inside the intestines of termites and digests the wood for them. Neither organism can survive alone.

**2** The clownfish hides among the tentacles of the _____ and feeds it in return.

**3** The large grouper fish seeks out small _____ that eat parasites off its body and get a meal in return.

**4** Elf owls live in holes in the saguaro _____, without helping or harming it.

**5** Tiny shrimp ride around on the back of certain _____, and no harm is done.

**6** An example of mutualism is _____, which consists of a fungus living with algae.

**7** The yucca plant depends on the yucca _____ to pollinate it; the moth drinks the nectar.

# Ecosystems Recycle Chemicals

ECOLOGY

Important chemicals such as carbon, nitrogen, and phosphorus are part of all living things. Carbon dioxide is released into the atmosphere by the respiration of animals. Then it enters the food chain through photosynthesis. Plants absorb nitrogen and phosphorus compounds from the soil. Decomposers return them to the soil again. All ecosystems recycle these important chemicals.

Root nodules of legumes make nitrates.

Weathering of rocks releases phosphorus.

Read each statement. Write **T** if the statement is true or **F** if it is false.

**1** _____ Plant leaves absorb nitrogen from the air.

**2** _____ Special bacteria living in the roots of legumes combine nitrogen with oxygen to make nitrates.

**3** _____ The weathering of rocks releases phosphorus and it dissolves in water.

**4** _____ Nitrogen compounds are essential for making plant and animal proteins.

**5** _____ Animals get needed carbon from eating plants or other animals.

**6** _____ Plants return a lot of carbon dioxide to the air through photosynthesis.

**7** _____ Plant roots absorb phosphorus and nitrogen compounds along with water.

**8** _____ When plants and animals die, decomposers return nitrogen and phosphorus to the soil.

**9** _____ Carbon is used to make proteins, fats, and carbohydrates.

**10** _____ Humans are able to manufacture their own carbon, nitrogen, and phosphorus.

Name _____ Date _____

# Renewable Resources

### NATURAL RESOURCES

**Renewable resources** are ones that we have in an unlimited amount, or are recycled by nature, or that we can replace. We have a continuous supply of sunlight and wind. Nature recycles the earth's water. We can plant new forests and crops. And we can raise new animals. The sun, the wind, and water can all be used to produce energy. We use plants and animals to give us energy through the food we eat.

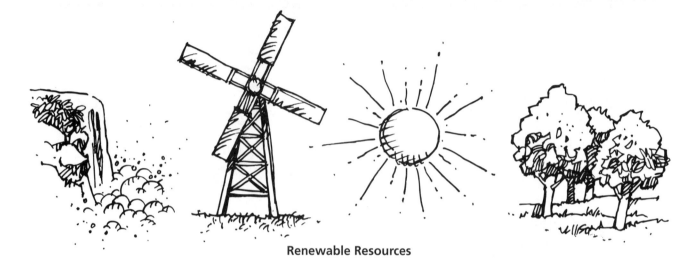

**Renewable Resources**

Use the words in the box to complete the sentences.

| renewable | sun | wind | water | wood | expand | electricity |
|---|---|---|---|---|---|---|

**1** In the U.S. today, about 8% of our energy is supplied from _____ resources.

**2** A long time ago, our main energy resource was burning _____.

**3** The _____ and the _____ are the cleanest renewable resources.

**4** Dams have been built in many places to use the power of falling _____ to give us energy.

**5** There are many places in the world where we can _____ our use of renewable resources.

**6** Most renewable resources are used to produce _____.

Name _____ Date _____

# Nonrenewable Resources

NATURAL RESOURCES

> **Nonrenewable** resources are ones we have in limited supply. We need to use them wisely because they will not last forever. All of the fossil fuels—coal, oil, and natural gas—are nonrenewable fuels. Nuclear fuel is also nonrenewable. All nonrenewable resources cause some pollution to the environment. However, we use them for 92% of our energy needs.

Energy Use Areas in the U.S.

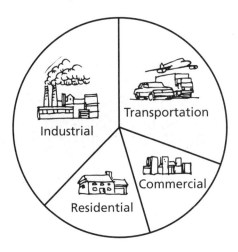

Major Sources of Electricity in the U.S.

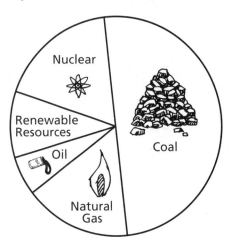

Use the two graphs to answer the questions.

**1** What area of our society uses the most energy? _____

**2** In which two areas of energy use could you personally help by conserving and not wasting energy? _____ and

_____

**3** Which nonrenewable resource is used the most to generate electricity?

_____

**4** Which nonrenewable resource is used the most for transportation needs?

_____

**5** Which nonrenewable resource is used the least to generate electricity?

_____

**6** Which two areas of society use more energy for lighting, heating, air-conditioning, and cooking? _____ and

_____

Science • 5–6 © 2005 Creative Teaching Press

Name _____  Date _____

# Coal

### NATURAL RESOURCES

**Coal** is formed from the remains of ancient swamp plants that lived millions of years ago. Large fern-like trees and giant rushes lived then. When these plants died, they fell into the water and gradually decayed. Through the years, more layers were added, increasing the pressure below. Eventually, coal was formed. Coal is mainly used for generating electricity, but it is also used for making steel, cement, and other products.

**Ancient Coal Swamp**

**Coal**

Read each statement. Write **T** if the statement is true or **F** if it is false.

**1** _____ Ancient swamp plants slowly decayed and turned into peat, the first step in making coal.

**2** _____ Today, coal is mainly used for manufacturing steel.

**3** _____ With time and pressure, peat turns into lignite, or brown coal.

**4** _____ In the United States, coal is our most plentiful fossil fuel.

**5** _____ Burning coal creates air pollution.

**6** _____ Coal formation started even before there were dinosaurs on the earth.

**7** _____ Anthracite coal will turn into bituminous, or soft coal.

**8** _____ As hard coal is formed, more moisture and impurities are removed by time and pressure.

**9** _____ Coal is used to help produce many products.

**10** _____ Most of the coal is deposited within the earth's crust and we have to build mines to dig it out.

Name _____ Date _____

# Oil and Natural Gas

### Natural Resources

> Oil and natural gas were formed from the remains of microscopic ocean organisms called **plankton.** Sometimes we find oil and natural gas together; other times each one is found separately. They are very useful fossil fuels. Oil is used to make gasoline and a variety of other fuels, as well as many household products. Natural gas is primarily used for heating buildings and for cooking.

**Oil**

**Natural Gas**

Write **O** if the sentence describes oil, **G** if it describes natural gas, or **B** if it describes both oil and natural gas.

**1** _____ It is a nonrenewable fossil fuel.

**2** _____ It is colorless and odorless when it comes out of the ground.

**3** _____ It is used to make gasoline, diesel, and jet fuel.

**4** _____ It is used for heating homes and buildings and for cooking food.

**5** _____ It is the cleanest fossil fuel to use.

**6** _____ It is used to make plastic, crayons, asphalt, acrylic, and polyester fabrics.

**7** _____ It is formed from the remains of microscopic ocean plankton organisms.

**8** _____ It must be refined and separated into various components before it can be used.

**9** _____ We drill down into the ground to find deposits of it.

**10** _____ A blue color and a smell are added to it before distribution to make it safer to use.

Name _____ Date _____

# Geothermal Energy

NATURAL RESOURCES

**Geothermal energy** comes from the heat within the earth. In places where magma pushes up closer to the surface, a lot of heat can be produced. This can heat underground water beyond the boiling point. Some may gush out of geysers, or bubble up in hot springs. However, most underground water stays trapped under the rock layers. We can drill down to find the trapped hot water and use it to generate electricity.

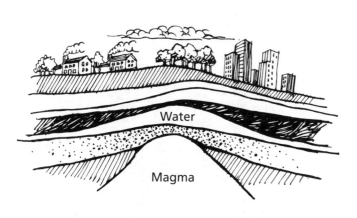

Put a ✓ by all the sentences that describe geothermal energy.

**1** _____ It is a renewable energy resource.

**2** _____ It causes air pollution.

**3** _____ It destroys the surrounding land.

**4** _____ It is energy from deep within the earth.

**5** _____ It cannot be used everywhere.

**6** _____ It can be used to generate electricity.

**7** _____ It is available twenty-four hours a day.

**8** _____ Its power plants cannot be located near cities.

**9** _____ It would create large amounts of waste material.

**10** _____ It would decrease our dependence on the use of fossil fuels.

Name _____ Date _____

# Wind Energy

### Natural Resources

The sun heats the earth's land, water, and air. This creates winds. Throughout humankind's history, people have used the power of the wind. The wind has helped ships sail around the world and powered windmills that crush grain or pump water. Modern windmills, called **wind turbines,** are used to generate electricity. They cannot be used everywhere or at all times, but wind turbines can produce a lot of energy.

Write **A** if the sentence describes an advantage of using wind energy or **D** if it describes a disadvantage of using wind energy.

**1** _____ Modern wind turbines can have blades up to 200 feet (61 m) long to catch more wind.

**2** _____ Wind energy is a renewable energy source.

**3** _____ Wind turbines cannot be used during storms or periods of very high winds.

**4** _____ One large turbine can produce enough electricity to power a small town.

**5** _____ Sometimes wind turbines can create television interference.

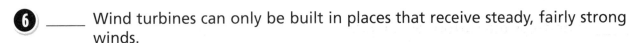

**Wind Turbine**

**6** _____ Wind turbines can only be built in places that receive steady, fairly strong winds.

**7** _____ Some people think wind turbines make the landscape look ugly.

**8** _____ Wind energy plants are as efficient at producing electricity as most other power plants.

**9** _____ Farmers can plant crops around a wind turbine after it has been installed.

**10** _____ Wind energy does not pollute the air.

Science • 5–6 © 2005 Creative Teaching Press

Name _____ Date _____

# Solar and Nuclear Energy

### NATURAL RESOURCES

**Solar energy** uses the power of the sun to heat water for homes or buildings and to generate electricity. Solar panels absorb the sun's heat, which is then transferred to water storage tanks. Solar cells use the sun's energy to generate electricity. **Nuclear energy** is produced from the splitting or "fission" of uranium atoms. This releases enough heat to boil water into steam. The steam is used to power electric generators.

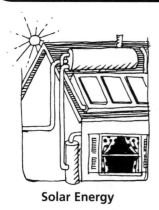

**Solar Energy**

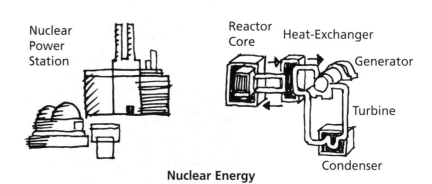

**Nuclear Energy**

Write **S** if the sentence describes solar energy, **N** if it describes nuclear energy, or **B** if it describes both solar and nuclear energy.

**1** _____ This type of energy plant is expensive to build.

**2** _____ This type of energy is renewable.

**3** _____ This type of energy is nonrenewable.

**4** _____ This type of energy does not pollute the environment.

**5** _____ This type of energy cannot be used twenty-four hours a day.

**6** _____ This type of energy can cause serious environmental pollution if not controlled properly.

**7** _____ This type of energy does not give off carbon dioxide as a waste product like fossil fuels do.

**8** _____ This type of energy cannot be used in an individual home.

**9** _____ This type of energy cannot be efficiently used in every part of the country.

**10** _____ This type of energy will probably be used more in the future.

Name _____ Date _____

# Air Pollution

NATURAL RESOURCES

Smoke from factories and exhaust fumes from automobiles are the main sources of air pollution. The excess carbon dioxide gas given off from burning fossil fuels traps some of the sun's heat in our atmosphere. This contributes to global warming. Gases containing sulfur dioxide and nitrogen oxides, produced by burning fossil fuels, create acid rain. Acid rain damages plants, animals, and even buildings.

Read each statement. Write **T** if the statement is true or **F** if it is false.

**1** _____ Air pollution affects our health.

**2** _____ You can reduce air pollution by conserving electricity.

**3** _____ Particles in smoke mix with the air to create smog.

**4** _____ Factory smokestacks and car exhaust cause most of our air pollution.

**5** _____ If you stay inside, you will not be exposed to polluted air.

**6** _____ Clearing forested land and burning the trees does not cause air pollution.

**7** _____ Acid rain forms when sulfur dioxide and nitrogen oxides mix with water and oxygen in the air.

**8** _____ Air pollution can affect the weather.

**9** _____ Anti-smog devices are required on cars to help reduce air pollution.

**10** _____ If you live far from factories, you will not be exposed to air pollution.

# Clean Drinking Water

NATURAL RESOURCES

It is difficult to find water clean enough to drink. Underground water can be obtained by digging wells. Surface water can be collected from natural springs or rainwater. The rainwater fills reservoirs, some of which form lakes that are also used for recreation. The water is sent to a purification plant where it is treated to make it clean and safe. Clean drinking water now flows through pipes to homes and buildings.

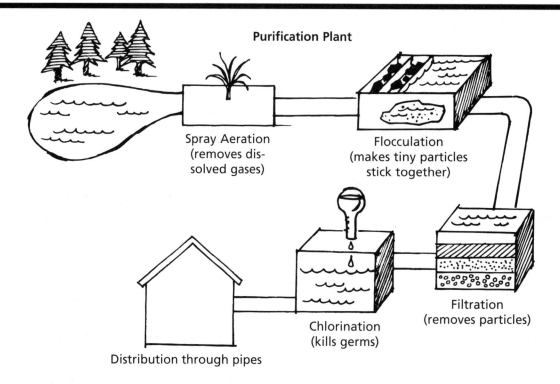

**Purification Plant**

Spray Aeration
(removes dis-
solved gases)

Flocculation
(makes tiny particles
stick together)

Filtration
(removes particles)

Chlorination
(kills germs)

Distribution through pipes

Number the sentences from 1 to 7 to show the order of how we obtain clean drinking water.

_____ Chlorine is added to kill germs.

_____ Rainwater collects in reservoirs.

_____ Chemicals are added to make very tiny particles stick together (flocculation).

_____ Water is sent to the purification plant.

_____ Clean, safe water is sent through pipes to homes and buildings.

_____ Water is now filtered to remove large and small particles and impurities.

_____ Water is mixed with air to remove unwanted dissolved gases.

*Science • 5–6* © 2005 Creative Teaching Press

Name _____ Date _____

# Pollution Puzzle

## NATURAL RESOURCES

Complete the puzzle. Use the words in the box if you need help. The word in the highlighted box is the key word.

| | | | | | |
|---|---|---|---|---|---|
| runoff | ground | litter | pesticides | drains | sewage |
| fertilizer | outflow | carbon | unlawful | dioxide | |

**1** Water pollutants can soak into the _____.

**2** Excess _____ from farmland washes into rivers where it causes pollution.

**3** Some factories release contaminated water in the _____ from their processing.

**4** It is _____ to flush leftover paint down a toilet because it pollutes the water.

**5** The release of _____ dioxide gas from burning fossil fuels causes global warming.

**6** Fumes of sulfur _____ from burning fossil fuels can cause acid rain.

**7** Spilled waste from broken _____ pipes causes water pollution.

**8** Used motor oil and other chemicals dumped down storm _____ pollute ocean water.

**9** If farmers spray too many _____ on their crops, the extra washes away and pollutes the water.

**10** Some people drop trash, known as _____, on the ground or in lakes and rivers.

**11** When sprinklers are on too long, the water _____ from our grass carries pollutants.

Science • 5–6 © 2005 Creative Teaching Press

Name _____ Date _____

# Plate Tectonics

### Geology

The crust of the earth is not made of one solid piece of rock. Rather, it is more like a giant jigsaw puzzle. Pressure from the mantle below makes the plates move. Scientists study the movements, known as **plate tectonics,** to learn more about how the surface of the earth changes. Plates can spread apart or push into each other. One may slide sideways past another, or one piece can get pushed under the edge of another.

Use the words in the box to complete the sentences.

| | | | | | | |
|---|---|---|---|---|---|---|
| spreading | colliding | subducts | sliding | plates | mantle | crust |

**1** The thin outer layer of the earth is called the _____.

**2** The Nazca plate and the South American plate are

_____, which pushes up the Andes Mountains.

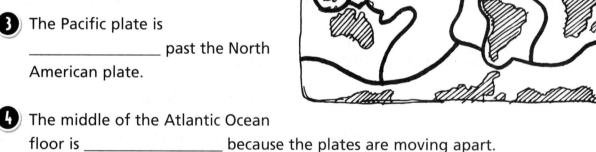

**3** The Pacific plate is _____ past the North American plate.

**4** The middle of the Atlantic Ocean floor is _____ because the plates are moving apart.

**5** An oceanic plate _____ when it bends down and slides under the edge of a continental plate.

**6** The _____ move because of the pressure on the crust from the _____ below.

Science • 5–6 © 2005 Creative Teaching Press

Name _____ Date _____

# Earthquakes

### GEOLOGY

We feel sudden movements of the earth's crust as earthquakes. Most earthquakes occur along the edges of the crust's plates. This is where the major fault lines are located. The place where the plates break apart is called the **focus**. On the surface of the earth, directly above the focus, is the epicenter of the earthquake. The P-waves travel quickly out from the epicenter. They are followed by the slower S-waves.

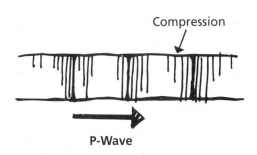

Compression

**P-Wave**

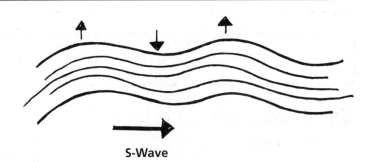

**S-Wave**

Read each statement. Write **T** if the statement is true or **F** if it is false.

1. _____ P-waves are compression waves, which push the crust together and pull it apart as they travel.

2. _____ Seismographs record the P-waves and S-waves to give us the magnitude of the earthquake.

3. _____ S-waves move the earth's crust up and down.

4. _____ P-waves travel at a little more than half the speed of S-waves.

5. _____ Seismographs from three locations are studied to calculate the epicenter of an earthquake.

6. _____ After the P- and S-waves, you may feel a "ground roll," which can cause a lot of damage.

7. _____ Scientists are able to accurately predict when earthquakes might occur.

8. _____ The area around the epicenter of an earthquake usually experiences the most damage.

9. _____ An earthquake that occurs under the ocean can cause a tsunami, or tidal wave.

10. _____ Most earthquakes start very deep in the earth, at least 150 miles (241 km) down.

Name _____ Date _____

# Where Do Earthquakes Happen?

GEOLOGY

Although almost all of the United States is located on the North American plate, the frequency of earthquakes varies a lot from region to region. Portions of the West Coast are on the edge of the Pacific plate, which is why this region experiences more earthquakes. However, smaller surface faults can be found scattered over wide areas of the country. Earthquakes are possible almost anywhere.

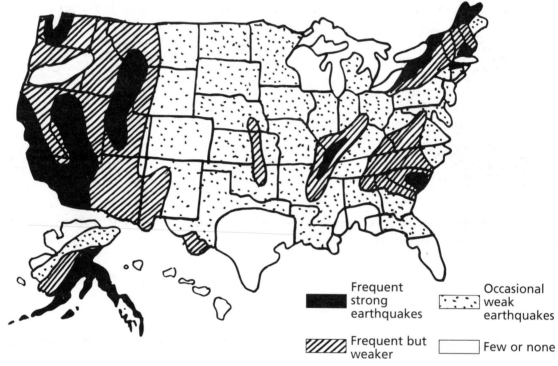

Frequent strong earthquakes

Frequent but weaker

Occasional weak earthquakes

Few or none

Use the map to answer the questions.

**1** Which area has more earthquakes, the Great Plains or New England?

_____

**2** Name two states that hardly ever have earthquakes. _____ and

_____

**3** Which state has areas showing all four frequencies of earthquakes?

_____

**4** Which southeastern state has the most earthquakes? _____

**5** Which state has more earthquakes, Utah or Colorado? _____

Science • 5–6 © 2005 Creative Teaching Press

Name _____ Date _____

# Types of Volcanoes

### GEOLOGY

There are three main types of volcanoes: composite, shield, and cinder cone. **Composite volcanoes** are the most common, as 60% of all volcanoes are this type. They erupt explosively, forming layers of ash and hardened lava with each eruption. **Shield volcanoes** erupt more gently, with the lava flowing more slowly. **Cinder cones** are the smallest volcanoes. They erupt very fast and then are completely finished.

| **Composite Volcano** | **Cinder Cone Volcano** | **Shield Volcano** |
|---|---|---|
|  |  |  |
| Inside View | Inside View | Inside View |
|  |  |  |

Write **C** if the sentence describes a composite volcano, **S** if it describes a shield volcano, or **A** if it describes a cinder cone volcano.

**1** _____ This type erupts violently, with more viscous lava and ashes, which eventually form a mountain.

**2** _____ This one is a wide-bodied volcano, with more gentle, thinner lava flows.

**3** _____ This type is the most common volcano.

**4** _____ This type forms large deposits of basalt, often in smooth ropey formations called pahoehoe.

**5** _____ This type erupts quickly, creating a hill made of many small pieces of hardened lava.

**6** _____ A famous volcano of this type erupted in Parícutin, Mexico in 1945.

**7** _____ Mt. Fuji, Mt. Vesuvius, and Mount St. Helens are examples of this type of volcano.

**8** _____ This type of volcano can be found in Hawaii.

**9** _____ This type forms tuff, pumice, and pea-sized pieces of basalt.

Name _____ Date _____

# Moving Magma in the Mantle

GEOLOGY

The mantle lies beneath the crust of the earth. The crust and the upper part of the mantle are composed of hardened rock. Together they are called the **lithosphere.** Below this is a semi-molten layer, called the **asthenosphere,** which mixes and moves very slowly. The hot material located in the mantle flows upward, where it cools and begins to sink. These convection currents within the mantle exert pressure on the earth's crust. This causes the movements known as plate tectonics.

Read each statement. Write **T** if the statement is true or **F** if it is false.

**1** _____ Geologists think the lithosphere "floats" on top of the asthenosphere.

**2** _____ The convection currents in the mantle are mainly caused by heat coming from the core.

**3** _____ It takes about one million years for the magma to complete one circular convection flow.

**4** _____ The deep mantle is composed of material with a lighter density than the outer mantle.

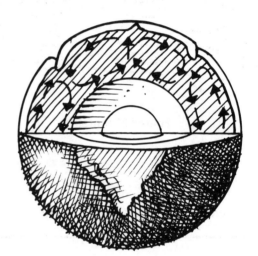

**5** _____ The convection currents in the mantle cause the plates of the crust to move.

**6** _____ Cooler material in the asthenosphere rises towards the lithosphere.

**7** _____ It takes about 200 million years for the magma to complete one circular convection flow.

**8** _____ The convection currents in the mantle help to create ocean floor trenches and ridges.

**9** _____ When the moving magma reaches a weaker spot below the crust, volcanoes may form.

**10** _____ The deep mantle is mostly solid.

Name _____ Date _____

# Faulting and Folding

GEOLOGY

The movements within the mantle exert tremendous pressure on the crust. The layers of rock that compose the crust are not all alike. Some are very brittle, while others are more flexible. Layers that cannot bend under the pressure from the mantle will crack and break. The two sides of the crack can slip away from each other at different angles. This is called **faulting. Folding** means the rock layers bend and wrinkle.

**Folded Mountains**                    **Fault-Block Mountains**

Use the words in the box to complete the sentences.

| tension | compression | shear | temperature | flexible | brittle | composition |
|---------|-------------|-------|-------------|----------|---------|-------------|

**1** _____ forces cause faulting by pulling rock layers apart.

**2** _____ forces make rock layers slide sideways, parallel to each other.

**3** Forces that squeeze rock layers together, called _____, cause faulting and folding.

**4** Rock layers that are more _____ will undergo folding.

**5** Rock layers that are more _____ will undergo faulting.

**6** Whether a rock layer will bend or crack depends on its _____ and _____.

# Water Shapes the Land

### GEOLOGY

Moving water causes the greatest amount of erosion. As rainwater runs off the land, it carries with it particles of soil and bits of broken rock. Heavy rains cause mudslides in some areas. As rivers flow downstream, they wear away the sides of the riverbed, widening it, and sometimes changing the course of the river. Oceans erode the land along the shore and deposit sand in other places.

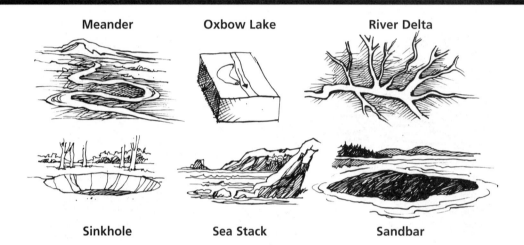

| Meander | Oxbow Lake | River Delta |
| Sinkhole | Sea Stack | Sandbar |

Match each item to its description.

**1** _____ River flowing downstream creates sweeping bends

**2** _____ Sediments build up at the mouth of a river and form this

**3** _____ The Colorado River carved this huge formation

**4** _____ Groundwater dissolves limestone rock and forms this

**5** _____ As rivers age, a winding path may eventually cause this to form

**6** _____ Groundwater creates a sunken area of land

**7** _____ Ocean waves deposit sand just offshore to form this

**8** _____ Deposits of sand at the ocean's edge widen this

**9** _____ Ocean waves erode headland, leaving an isolated mass of rock

**A.** a cave

**B.** meanders

**C.** a beach

**D.** a sinkhole

**E.** a sea stack

**F.** a sandbar

**G.** a delta

**H.** Grand Canyon

**I.** an oxbow lake

Name _____ Date _____

# Glaciers

GEOLOGY

**Glaciers** are huge masses of ice. They usually form from large accumulations of snow that never melt. When the weight of the whole formation becomes too much to remain stationary, the glacier begins to move. It moves a few inches each day. Glaciers form in valleys between mountains or at the poles. As they slide downhill, glaciers can carve new peaks and change the shape of the valley.

Number the sentences from 1 to 7 to show the order of how a valley glacier forms and moves down a mountain to the sea.

_____ Broken rock pieces become embedded in the glacier and act like a file as they scrape over the land.

_____ Snow accumulates in large amounts for several years, with very little melting.

_____ As the glacier gets farther downhill, cracks called crevasses form on the surface and sides.

_____ The weight of the snow causes the lower layers to melt and refreeze into a solid mass of ice.

_____ When the glacier finally reaches the sea, pieces break off the front end, forming icebergs.

_____ Eventually, the weight of the glacier makes the bottom begin to melt.

_____ Now the glacier slowly slides downhill, gouging out the rock beneath it and carrying it along.

Name _____ Date _____

# Soil Formation

### GEOLOGY

Rocks in the earth's crust gradually wear down and break apart. This process is called **weathering.** The sun, water, ice, wind, temperature changes, plant roots, and movement of animals all cause rocks to break and crumble very slowly. Eventually, rocks become sand grains. Plants and animals die and decay, and then they form a material known as **humus.** When humus is mixed with crumbled rock and sand, fertile soil is created.

Write **H** if the sentence describes the humus layer, **T** if it describes the topsoil, **S** if it describes the subsoil, or **B** if it describes the bedrock layer.

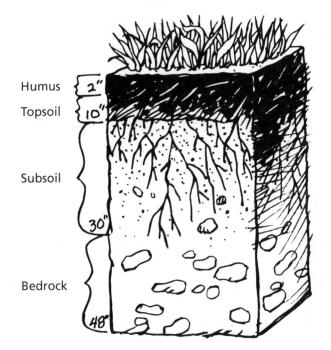

Humus  2"
Topsoil  10"
Subsoil  30"
Bedrock  48"

❶ _____ This upper layer contains plant roots, bacteria, fungi, and soil animals.

❷ _____ This middle layer contains the tips of plant roots, and it is not as fertile.

❸ _____ This very thin layer is rich with decayed organic matter from dead plants and animals.

❹ _____ This lower layer contains more original rock that hasn't been weathered much.

❺ _____ This layer of soil is the best for growing plants.

❻ _____ This is the thickest layer.

❼ _____ This layer has minerals that have washed down from above.

Science • 5–6 © 2005 Creative Teaching Press

Name _____ Date _____

# Types of Soil

GEOLOGY

As rocks weather, they break into pieces of different sizes. Larger rock pieces that are mixed in with the soil are called **pebbles**. The soil itself is made from three smaller-sized pieces: sand, silt, and clay. In almost any soil sample there will be combinations of these three types of particles. The best soil is a pure loam, which has about an equal percentage of each of the three components.

| Soil Type | Approximate % Sand Particles | Approximate % Silt Particles | Approximate % Clay Particles |
|---|---|---|---|
| Various Loam Soils | 25–50 | 25–50 | 25–50 |
| Clay-Rich Soils | 0–45 | 0–55 | 35–100 |
| Sandy Soils | 50–100 | 0–55 | 0–55 |
| Silty Soils | 0–50 | 40–100 | 0–50 |

Read each statement. Write **T** if the statement is true or **F** if it is false.

**1** _____ Powdery clay particles are the smallest particles that form soil.

**2** _____ Sand helps to keep the soil from getting packed down.

**3** _____ Sand particles help the soil hold water.

**4** _____ Clay soils have at least 35% clay particles.

**5** _____ Clay soils absorb water more slowly and can become hard-packed upon drying out.

**6** _____ Silt particles, which are like fine dirt, are larger than sand particles.

**7** _____ Loam soils have more of a balance of the three soil particles.

**8** _____ Silty soils contain 40–100% silt particles.

**9** _____ A soil with 35% sand particles would be classified as a type of sandy soil.

**10** _____ You will find soil with 85–100% sand at the beach.

Science • 5-6 © 2005 Creative Teaching Press

Name _____ Date _____

# The Earth's Atmosphere

WEATHER

The **atmosphere** is a thick layer of air that surrounds and protects the earth. It is composed of five layers: the troposphere, stratosphere, mesosphere, thermosphere (ionosphere), and exosphere. Almost all of our weather occurs in the troposphere because it contains a lot of water vapor. The troposphere extends upwards 6–10 miles (10–16 km).

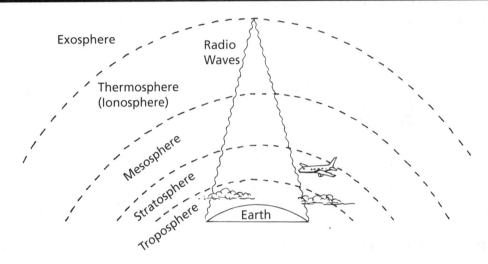

Which layer does each sentence describe? Write **T** for troposphere, **S** for stratosphere, **M** for mesosphere, **I** for ionosphere (thermosphere), or **E** for exosphere.

**1** _____ Most weather conditions, such as clouds and storms, occur in this layer.

**2** _____ This layer has the coldest temperatures of the atmosphere.

**3** _____ The sun's ultraviolet rays hit this layer and cause the air particles to become electrically charged.

**4** _____ This layer contains almost all of the water vapor in the air.

**5** _____ Jet airplane pilots like to fly here because the sky is cloudless and clear.

**6** _____ There is almost no air here, as this layer extends out toward outer space.

**7** _____ Ozone, which absorbs harmful ultraviolet rays from the sun, is found in this layer.

**8** _____ This layer reflects radio waves back to earth, letting us receive signals from far away.

**9** _____ This faraway layer contains the Van Allen radiation belt.

*Science • 5–6* © 2005 Creative Teaching Press

Name _____  Date _____

# What Causes the Weather?

WEATHER

The four main factors that give us all our weather are the sun, air pressure, humidity, and the wind. The sun is the most important, because it heats the air and the earth. Changes in air pressure tell us that the weather is changing some and may even indicate a storm is coming. **Humidity** measures the amount of moisture in the air. Uneven heating and cooling of the earth's land and water creates winds.

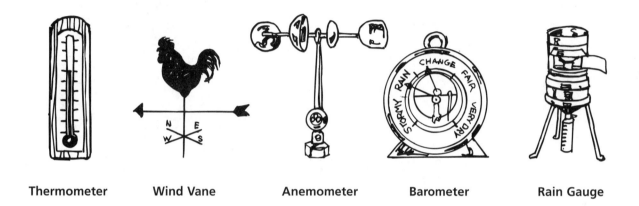

| Thermometer | Wind Vane | Anemometer | Barometer | Rain Gauge |

Read each statement. Write **T** if the statement is true or **F** if it is false.

**1** _____ The weather changes through the seasons because the earth rotates at a tilt.

**2** _____ Thermometers are used to measure how much the sun has heated the air.

**3** _____ A wind vane tells us in which direction a wind is blowing.

**4** _____ A barometer is a weather instrument for measuring humidity.

**5** _____ Anemometers measure wind speed.

**6** _____ Big changes in air pressure indicate the weather is changing more dramatically.

**7** _____ A rain gauge is used to measure the amount of rainfall.

**8** _____ Meteorologists study changes in the air to try to forecast the weather.

**9** _____ The humidity stays about the same throughout the day.

**10** _____ Scientists can accurately forecast the weather weeks ahead of time.

Name _____ Date _____

# Convection Currents in the Air

WEATHER

The sun heats the earth and the air. However, land areas heat up and cool off faster than water areas. This creates different temperatures in the air above these areas. Warm air rises up into the sky. As it gets higher, it begins to cool off. Then the cool air begins to sink. This movement of air is called **convection**. The rotation of the earth adds to the effect. The moving air currents create winds.

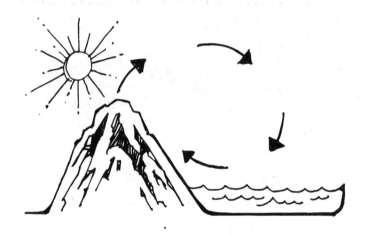

**A Convection Current**

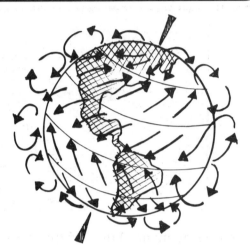

**Wind Patterns on the Earth**

Use the words in the box to complete the sentences.

| faster | wind | sink | convection | rises | rotation | poles | equator |
|--------|------|------|------------|-------|----------|-------|---------|

**1** Land areas of the earth heat up _____ than water areas.

**2** As air gets warm, it _____, and as it cools it begins to _____.

**3** Cold air at the _____ of the earth moves outward.

**4** The circular movement of air is called _____.

**5** The _____ of the earth causes the convection patterns to have a slanted shape.

**6** The moving air currents caused by convection create the _____.

**7** Areas of calm air are found in the doldrums, located around the _____.

Science • 5–6 © 2005 Creative Teaching Press

Name _____ Date _____

# Land and Sea Breezes

WEATHER

Land and sea breezes are winds at the seashore that blow in one direction during the day and then in the opposite direction at night. During the day, the land heats up faster than the ocean, causing warm air to rise over the land. Cooler air over the ocean moves in to take its place. As night approaches, the land cools off faster, and the cooler air over the land moves out to sea. Land breezes are weaker than sea breezes.

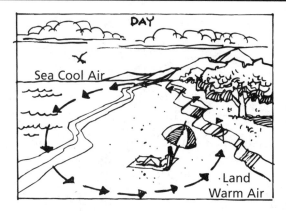
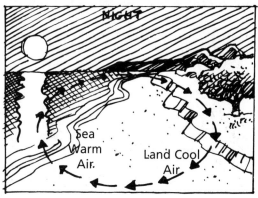

Read each statement. Write **T** if the statement is true or **F** if it is false.

1. _____ A breeze or wind is always named for the direction that it comes from.

2. _____ At night at the beach the air over the water is cooler than the air over the land.

3. _____ Sea breezes usually die down at sunset.

4. _____ Cooler air moves in closer to the ground.

5. _____ Land breezes blow during the day.

6. _____ Land and sea breezes blow in opposite directions.

7. _____ The unequal heating and cooling of land and water causes sea breezes and land breezes.

8. _____ At night the air over the land is blowing out towards the sea.

9. _____ Land and sea breezes make the temperatures less extreme near the seashore.

10. _____ During the day, the warm air over the land moves farther inland, away from the beach.

Name _____ Date _____

# Air Pressure

WEATHER

Believe it or not, the air is pressing down on you. You don't usually notice it because the air inside your body is balancing the air pressure outside. If your ears have ever popped, then they were adjusting to a change in air pressure. The **barometer** is an instrument that measures air pressure. Colder air is heavier than warm air, and as colder air sinks it exerts a higher pressure on the earth than warm air.

Use the words in the box to complete the sentences.

sea level
low
high
better
worse
air pressure
barometer
lower

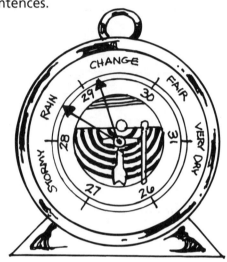

**Aneroid Barometer**

① The air pressure at _____ is almost 15 lbs. per square inch (1 kg/sq cm).

② Cold air masses have a _____ pressure.

③ Warm air masses have a _____ pressure.

④ The instrument used to measure air pressure is called a _____.

⑤ If the air pressure is rising, that is an indication that the weather will get _____.

⑥ When the air pressure is falling, that is an indication that the weather will get _____.

⑦ It is easier to feel changes in the temperature or wind than it is to feel the _____.

⑧ As you go up a mountain, the air pressure gets a little _____.

Science • 5–6 © 2005 Creative Teaching Press

Name _____ Date _____

# Humidity

### WEATHER

The amount of moisture in the air is called **humidity.** The air is like a sponge soaking up moisture, except that the moisture in the air is mainly invisible water vapor. When the air cannot hold any more moisture, we get condensation. Warm air can hold more moisture than cold air. The amount of moisture in the air is expressed as the relative humidity. It tells us the percentage of the air that is full of water vapor.

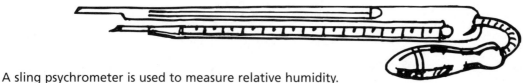

A sling psychrometer is used to measure relative humidity.

Read each statement. Write **T** if the statement is true or **F** if it is false.

**1** _____ A sling psychrometer contains a wet and dry thermometer and is used to measure relative humidity.

**2** _____ We feel the humidity more on cold days.

**3** _____ When the air is completely saturated with water vapor, the relative humidity is 100%.

**4** _____ As air gets cooler, the relative humidity increases.

**5** _____ Some days the air is so humid it makes you feel sticky.

**6** _____ The temperature below which air must be cooled for condensation to occur is the dew point.

**7** _____ When condensation occurs we get rainfall.

**8** _____ As you go up a mountain, the relative humidity decreases as the temperature changes.

**9** _____ The humidity is always higher in tropical regions near the equator.

**10** _____ Water vapor is water in the form of an invisible gas.

Science • 5–6 © 2005 Creative Teaching Press

Name _____ Date _____

# Precipitation

### WEATHER

Precipitation includes all the forms of moisture that fall out of the sky. It may be rain, drizzle, sleet, glaze, snow, or hail. Clouds form when condensation takes place. When the clouds cannot hold any more water, we get **precipitation.** The temperatures of the air and on the ground determine the type of precipitation that forms. Rain is the most common form of precipitation. We measure rainfall with a rain gauge.

**Rain**
(Water drops)

**Sleet**
(Frozen rain)

**Snow**
(Frozen water vapor)

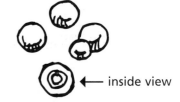

← inside view

**Hail**
(Layers of frozen rain)

Match each form of precipitation to its description.

**1** _____ Freezing water vapor inside clouds makes this

**2** _____ Rain that freezes on the way down

**3** _____ Very tiny water droplets that fall slowly

**4** _____ Larger water droplets that fall out of clouds

**5** _____ Raindrops falling on frozen ground form this

**6** _____ Raindrops that get caught in updrafts, freeze, and build up layers of ice to form round pellets

**7** _____ Moisture that condenses on the grass and ground

**8** _____ Freezing water vapor that condenses at ground level

**A.** drizzle

**B.** glaze

**C.** snow

**D.** sleet

**E.** rain

**F.** dew

**G.** hail

**H.** frost

Science • 5–6 © 2005 Creative Teaching Press

Name _____ Date _____

# Reading the Clouds

WEATHER

You can tell a lot about the weather if you know how to read the clouds. The three basic types of clouds are cirrus, cumulus, and stratus. **Cirrus** clouds may indicate a distant storm, but your current weather will be fair. **Cumulus** clouds indicate fair weather. **Stratus** clouds indicate a chance of drizzle or light snow at higher elevations. If a cloud has *nimbo* or *nimbus* in its name, it is a storm cloud with lots of rain.

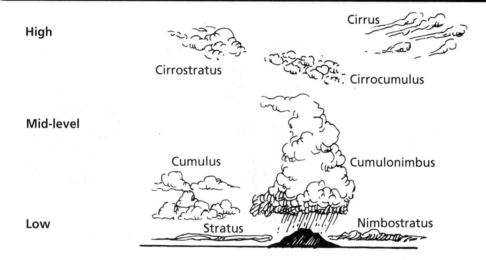

**High**

Cirrus

Cirrostratus

Cirrocumulus

**Mid-level**

Cumulus

Cumulonimbus

**Low**

Stratus

Nimbostratus

Match each type of cloud to its description.

**1** _____ High, thin clouds made of ice crystals that form a halo around the sun or moon; indicate coming rain or snow

**2** _____ Towering clouds with a dark base; bring thunderstorms

**3** _____ High, thin, wispy clouds made of ice crystals; weather is all right for now

**4** _____ Big, fluffy, white, mid-level clouds that mean fair weather

**5** _____ Low, gray clouds that form a blanket over the sky

**6** _____ Low, dark, gray storm clouds that bring continuous rain

**7** _____ Group of small, round, fluffy clouds; chance of rain in 15–20 hours

**A.** cumulonimbus

**B.** cirrus

**C.** nimbostratus

**D.** stratus

**E.** cumulus

**F.** cirrocumulus

**G.** cirrostratus

Name _____ Date _____

# Cold Fronts

WEATHER

A **cold front** is a moving mass of cold air that pushes into a warmer air mass. The cold air pushes under the warm air and makes it move up and out of the way. The front is the place where the two air masses meet. There is usually some rain or snow when a cold front moves in, but it generally does not last for a long time. The skies will clear and you will have colder weather for a while.

Cold front symbol

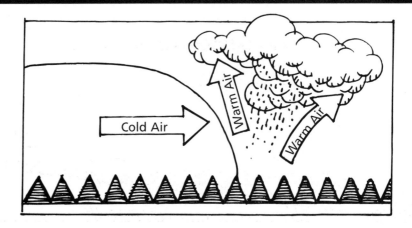

Put a ✓ by all the sentences that describe a cold front.

**1** _____ A cold front is an air mass with cold air in the front and warm air in the middle.

**2** _____ A cold front is a moving mass of cold air.

**3** _____ In a cold front, the cold air moves in on top of warm air and pushes it off to the side.

**4** _____ Cold fronts move in more quickly than warm fronts.

**5** _____ Sometimes cumulonimbus clouds form when a cold front moves in.

**6** _____ You usually get some rain or snow when a cold front moves in.

**7** _____ In the U.S., cold fronts usually move in from the north or northwest.

**8** _____ When a cold front moves in you will experience rain for many days.

**9** _____ After a cold air mass has moved in, the skies will clear and you will have much warmer weather.

**10** _____ The weather map symbol for a cold front is a row of solid triangles.

Name _____ Date _____

# Warm Fronts

A **warm front** is a moving mass of warm air that pushes into a colder air mass. The warm air is lighter and moves in on top of the cold air. The cold air gets pushed slowly off to the side. The slope of a warm front is very gradual, since it does not move in quickly. There will be some cirrus clouds at the beginning, then stratus clouds, and closest to the ground some nimbostratus clouds. These bring rain for several days.

Warm front symbol

Warm Air

Cirrus

Stratus

Nimbostratus

Cold Air

Rain

Put a ✓ by all the sentences that describe a warm front.

**1** _____ A warm front is a mass of warm air that moves into a region that has cooler air.

**2** _____ The edge or slope of a warm front is very gradual.

**3** _____ Warm fronts move in more quickly than cold fronts.

**4** _____ Masses of clouds form along the entire warm front as it moves in.

**5** _____ Cirrus clouds form up high as the front just begins to move in.

**6** _____ Nimbostratus clouds accompany a warm front and bring a lot of rain.

**7** _____ The rain from a warm front covers a small area.

**8** _____ Warm fronts in the U.S. tend to move towards the south and southwest.

**9** _____ After the rain clears, you will have warmer weather for a while.

**10** _____ The symbol for a warm front is a row of dark, rounded bumps.

# Thunderstorms

WEATHER

**Thunderstorms** are most common during late spring and summer in the eastern half of the U.S. They are small storms, but they can produce large quantities of rain, and even hail. They form when rising currents of moist, warm air are made to cool off rapidly. Cumulonimbus clouds grow to towering heights. Electrical charges build up within the cloud. Lightning and thunder are produced.

Use the words in the box to complete the sentences.

| lightning | thunder | cumulonimbus | warm | hail | rain | static | hours |
|---|---|---|---|---|---|---|---|

**1** Thunderstorms are small, strong storms that usually last a few

_____.

**2** Big _____ clouds form before a thunderstorm.

**3** Fast-rising air rubs against water droplets in the cloud, building up _____ electrical charges.

**4** Thunderstorms form when rising currents of _____, moist air are made to cool off rapidly.

**5** We see the electrical discharges from the cloud as _____.

**6** We hear _____, which is due to the lightning making the air heat up and expand.

**7** Thunderstorms drop a lot of _____ in a short time.

**8** If raindrops are caught in the updrafts, they can build up layers of ice and form

_____.

Science • 5–6 © 2005 Creative Teaching Press

# Hurricanes

WEATHER

**Hurricanes** are enormous, slow-moving storms that start out over the ocean. They form from low-pressure areas in the tropics. The warm air rises and begins to spiral. When the winds reach 74 mph (119 km/hr), it becomes a named hurricane. Fortunately, hurricanes travel forward very slowly, giving people in coastal regions time to prepare. Hurricanes can last for several weeks and can cause tremendous damage.

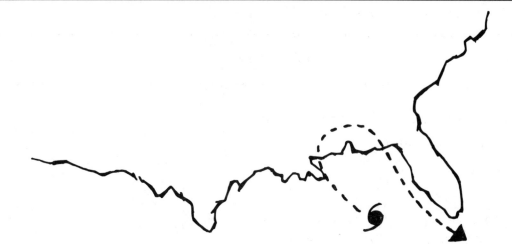

Read each statement. Write **T** if the statement is true or **F** if it is false.

**1** _____ The path of a hurricane can cover hundreds of miles.

**2** _____ Hurricanes travel forward at about 10–15 mph (16–24 kph).

**3** _____ The winds at the center of the hurricane are the strongest.

**4** _____ Hurricanes are very wet storms that drop lots of rain.

**5** _____ Hurricanes occur mainly in the winter months.

**6** _____ Meteorologists track the path of a hurricane and can issue warnings to people.

**7** _____ The most damage from a hurricane comes from its strong winds.

**8** _____ In some parts of the world, hurricanes are called typhoons.

**9** _____ Hurricanes lose strength when they move over the land.

**10** _____ Eventually, most hurricanes move back out to sea and blow themselves out.

Name _____ Date _____

# Tornadoes

WEATHER

> **Tornadoes** are small, extremely violent storms that form over dry land. They are common in the central part of the U.S. They are often associated with cumulonimbus clouds. The strong, whirling winds form a dark, funnel-shaped cloud. Tornadoes can reach speeds up to 500 mph (800 km/hr). The tornado follows an unpredictable path, destroying everything it touches. Fortunately, tornadoes only last 8–10 minutes.

Put a ✓ by the sentences that describe a tornado.

**1** _____ At the center of a tornado is an extremely low-pressure area.

**2** _____ Tornadoes start over a body of water.

**3** _____ Most tornadoes occur between spring and early summer.

**4** _____ Tornadoes cause damage because they cause homes and buildings to cave in on themselves.

**5** _____ The funnel-shaped cloud forms in the air and then touches down on the ground.

**6** _____ Tornadoes can pick up objects and hurl them out in a few minutes.

**7** _____ When a tornado passes over, people often hear a deafening roar from the winds.

**8** _____ Tornadoes travel forward at speeds ranging from 30–70 mph (48–112 km/hr).

**9** _____ People who live in tornado-prone areas often have a storm cellar for protection.

**10** _____ Meteorologists can predict the path of a tornado.

# Reading Weather Maps

WEATHER

Meteorologists use symbols to represent different aspects of the weather. The symbols can show the position of highs and lows, fronts, rain, cloudiness, and temperatures. This enables meteorologists to show a lot of data on a weather map. The maps are used to study current weather patterns and to predict how the weather might change in the near future.

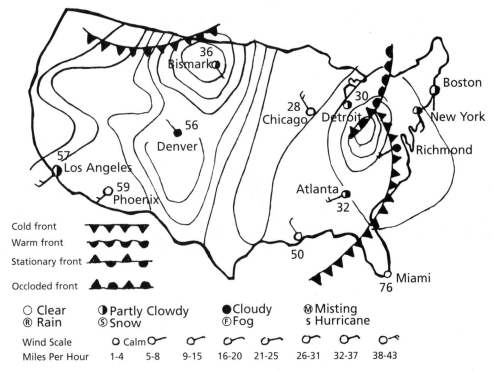

Cold front

Warm front

Stationary front

Occloded front

○ Clear     ◑ Partly Clowdy     ● Cloudy     Ⓜ Misting
Ⓡ Rain      Ⓢ Snow              Ⓕ Fog        s Hurricane

Wind Scale         ○ Calm
Miles Per Hour      1-4    5-8    9-15    16-20    21-25    26-31    32-37    38-43

Complete the tasks or answer the questions.

**1** Name a city where it is sunny and warm. _____

**2** Draw the symbol used to represent a partly cloudy sky. _____

**3** Name two cities where it is very cloudy. _____ and _____

**4** Which city has a high-pressure cell, Bismarck or Phoenix? _____

**5** What do the little "hockey stick" symbols extending out from a city's circle represent? _____

**6** What do all the lines across the weather map show? _____

**7** Describe the weather conditions for Atlanta: The temperature is _____. The cloud cover is _____. The winds are _____.

# Weather Words Rebus Puzzle

## WEATHER

Use the pictures to decode the weather words. Decode the name of clouds in the first three rebus puzzles.

**1** s + – in + tus =

**2** c + + ul + – brella – b =

**3** – cle + rus =

Decode the rebuses to answer the questions

**4** What does water do to get into the air?

– gg + va + – t + + e

**5** What supplies most of the water to the atmosphere?

O + – + – r + n =

**6** What is the atmosphere made of?

– ht + – fe =

**7** What is one of the four factors that causes our weather?

+ – and + 4 – fo + e =

**8** What is formed when water vapor near the ground changes into ice?

– g + – op =

Science • 5–6 © 2005 Creative Teaching Press

Name _____ Date _____

# The Solar System and the Universe

### OUTER SPACE

Believe it or not, our solar system is only a tiny speck in outer space. The word *universe* includes everything in outer space, most of which is just empty space. Scattered about are many galaxies, each one composed of millions of stars. Our solar system lies within the Milky Way galaxy. Our star, the sun, is at the center of the solar system. There are nine planets that orbit the sun.

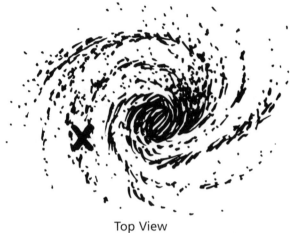

Top View                                    Side View

**Milky Way Galaxy**                         X = Solar System

Arrange all the outer space objects in order, from the largest to the smallest.

1 _____

2 _____

3 _____

4 _____

5 _____

6 _____

7 _____

8 _____

9 _____

| |
|---|
| Pluto |
| universe |
| solar system |
| Jupiter |
| galaxy |
| sun |
| Earth |
| Saturn |
| Earth's moon |

Name _____  Date _____

# The Sun

OUTER SPACE

The **sun** is an average-sized star. However, it is still very large. The sun could hold more than one million Earths inside it. It is the closest star to Earth. The sun is an enormous ball of hot gases. Three layers of gases form the atmosphere that surrounds the main body of the sun. Nuclear reactions take place inside the sun. They produce tremendous quantities of heat and light, which are released gradually over billions of years.

Match each item to its description.

**1** _____ Sunspots

**2** _____ Photosphere

**3** _____ Solar prominences

**4** _____ Radiation zone

**5** _____ Convection zone

**6** _____ Core

**7** _____ Corona

**8** _____ Gases found in the sun

**9** _____ Distance to the sun from Earth

A. mostly hydrogen, some helium

B. keeps energy moving to surface

C. storms on the surface; usually occur in 11-year cycles

D. halo of gases around the sun

E. huge fiery arms or loops extending from the sun's surface

F. inner layer of the sun's atmosphere; the part we see

G. thickest layer of the sun

H. where nuclear reactions occur

I. 93 million miles

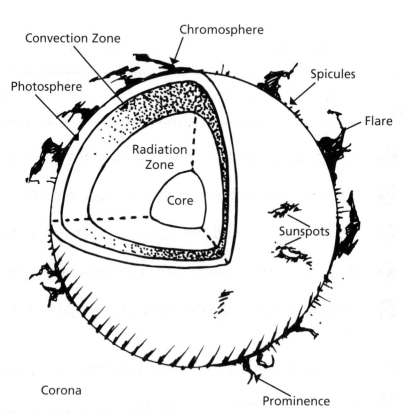

Science • 5–6 © 2005 Creative Teaching Press

Name _____ Date _____

# The Moon and the Tides

OUTER SPACE

The moon is Earth's closest neighbor in space. Earth's gravity attracts the moon, holding it in orbit. The moon's gravity, while weaker, does exert a pull on Earth. It mainly pulls on the oceans. This is what causes the tides. Twice each day, the oceans bulge a little, causing the water to wash up farther on the shore. Other areas have lower water levels. As Earth rotates, the site of high tide and low tide changes.

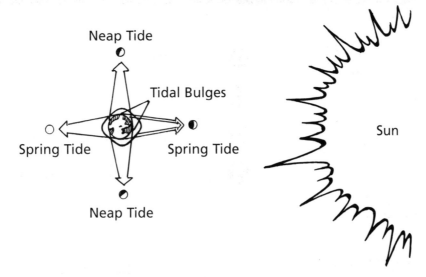

Use the words in the box to complete the sentences.

| tide | moon | high | low | twice | sun | opposite |

**1** The rise and fall of the ocean level along the shore is called the _____.

**2** The tides are mostly caused by the gravitational pull of the _____.

**3** When the moon and the _____ are lined up, we experience greater high tides.

**4** When our part of Earth faces the moon, we have _____ tides.

**5** When our part of Earth is at a right angle to the moon, we have _____ tides.

**6** We have periods of high and low tides _____ a day.

**7** If we are having a high tide, the _____ side of Earth has a high tide, too.

Name _____ Date _____

# Phases of the Moon

### OUTER SPACE

It is easy to see the moon, but it is much harder to understand where the moon is in relation to Earth and the sun. Remember, the moon doesn't produce any light. We see the sunlight that is reflected by the moon. We see a full moon when Earth is between the moon and the sun. We have a new moon when the moon is between the sun and Earth. If the sun, Earth, and the moon are in a straight line, we have an **eclipse.**

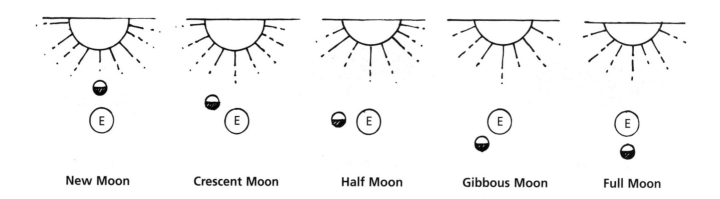

| **New Moon** | **Crescent Moon** | **Half Moon** | **Gibbous Moon** | **Full Moon** |

Read each statement. Write **T** if the statement is true or **F** if it is false.

**1** _____ We see a full moon when the sun is behind and a little above Earth.

**2** _____ We see a new moon, if at all, in the early morning and at sunset.

**3** _____ We always see the same side of the moon because it takes the moon one month to rotate.

**4** _____ It takes the moon one month to revolve around Earth.

**5** _____ Approximately one month after a new moon we will have a full moon.

**6** _____ Eclipses occur occasionally at the times of new moons and full moons.

**7** _____ The moon's orbit is not in the same 3-D plane as Earth's orbit around the sun.

**8** _____ We see a crescent moon right after a full moon.

**9** _____ Each night after a new moon we can see a little less of the moon lit up.

**10** _____ Half of the moon always receives light from the sun.

Science • 5–6 © 2005 Creative Teaching Press

Name _____ Date _____

# Galaxies

OUTER SPACE

**Galaxies** are enormous collections of stars, dust, and gas in space. A single galaxy has millions of stars. And there are billions of galaxies in outer space. Most galaxies have a spiral shape, but some are elliptical, and others have an irregular shape. Scientists think the irregularly shaped galaxies are younger. The spiral galaxies are larger in size. The Milky Way galaxy, which is a spiral galaxy, is 100,000 light years across.

**Spiral Galaxy**

**Elliptical Galaxy**

**Irregular Galaxy**

Write **S** if the sentence describes a spiral galaxy, **E** if it describes an elliptical galaxy, or **I** if it describes an irregular galaxy.

**1** _____ This is a younger galaxy with lots of dust and gas between the stars.

**2** _____ This is the most common type of galaxy.

**3** _____ This galaxy is believed to consist of mainly older stars.

**4** _____ The Milky Way is an example of this type of galaxy, where new stars are still forming.

**5** _____ This type of galaxy has no definite shape and is forming many very hot new stars.

**6** _____ This galaxy has an oblong shape and is no longer producing new stars.

**7** _____ This galaxy has a bulge-like hub in the center.

Name _____ Date _____

# Zodiac Constellations

OUTER SPACE

**Constellations** are groups of stars that people long ago thought resembled a picture. There are twelve zodiac constellations. They are located in a band that is a little above and below the path the sun takes as it revolves around the center of the Milky Way galaxy. Special names have been given to the zodiac constellations. We can see each one prominently in the sky for about a month during the year.

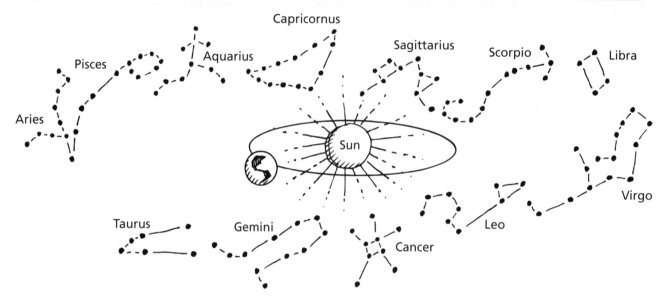

Use the words in the box to complete the sentences.

| imagined | easy | zodiac | not easy | astrologers | astronomers |
|---|---|---|---|---|---|

**1** Long ago, people _____ they saw pictures in the night sky.

**2** Grouping stars into constellations makes it _____ for scientists to describe their location in the sky.

**3** It is _____ to actually see the picture in a constellation.

**4** People known as _____ think they can foretell the future by reading the stars.

**5** Modern scientists who use mathematics to study the stars are called _____ .

**6** Each constellation of the _____ is more clearly visible for about one month.

Science • 5–6 © 2005 Creative Teaching Press

Name _____ Date _____

# Comets

OUTER SPACE

**Comets** are like dirty snowballs in space, except they do not contain water. Comets are made of rocks, dust, and frozen gases. They travel in large, oblong orbits around the sun. When a comet nears the sun, some of it melts and forms a long tail. The tail consists of the melted gases that were vaporized by the sun. When the comet moves farther away from the sun, the tail disappears. Eventually, comets will disintegrate.

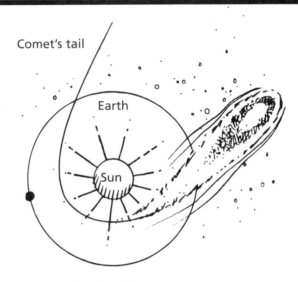

Comet's tail

Earth

Sun

Put a ✓ by the sentences that accurately describe a comet.

**1** _____ They travel in orbits with a shape similar to the planets of the solar system.

**2** _____ A comet's tail always faces away from the sun.

**3** _____ Comets form when pieces of a planet or moon break off.

**4** _____ We only see a comet when its orbit brings it close to Earth.

**5** _____ The tail can extend for millions of miles (kilometers).

**6** _____ The tail is so thin that you can see through it.

**7** _____ After many, many years, a comet will eventually disintegrate.

**8** _____ Comets are made of rock, dust, and frozen gases.

**9** _____ Comets travel at the same speed throughout their entire orbit.

**10** _____ Halley's comet returns every 76 years.

Name _____ Date _____

# Meteors and Asteroids

### OUTER SPACE

Meteors and asteroids are pieces of rocky material, or rock mixed with metal. **Asteroids** are much larger than meteors but smaller than planets. There is a belt of about 25,000 asteroids and meteors between Mars and Jupiter. **Meteors** that enter Earth's atmosphere usually burn up from the friction of the air. They appear as a bright streak across the sky. People call this a **shooting star.** A few have hit Earth.

**Asteroid**          **Meteor**          **Impact Crater on the Earth**

Write **M** if the sentence describes meteors, **A** if it describes asteroids, or **B** if it describes both meteors and asteroids.

**1** _____ These are very common, and several enter Earth's atmosphere every day.

**2** _____ These are pieces of space debris made of rock, or rock and metal material.

**3** _____ Many of these are found between Mars and Jupiter.

**4** _____ These are large, but they are not nearly as big as a planet.

**5** _____ These are very small in size compared to other objects in space.

**6** _____ Sometimes we see pretty "showers" of these at night.

**7** _____ Scientists are not sure how these were formed.

**8** _____ If these leave their orbit and crash into other space objects, broken bits can form meteors.

**9** _____ These get their name because they look like stars, and yet they are like little planets.

**10** _____ Some of these are as large as 100 miles (60 km) in diameter.

# Nebulae

### OUTER SPACE

A **nebula** is a huge cloud of dust and gases found in outer space. There are many nebulae within irregular and spiral galaxies. Some nebulae are bright and glow. Others are dark cloud shapes and can only be seen by the contrast of the bright sky surrounding them. Scientists believe they are places where stars begin to form. Some nebulae form from the remains of a **supernova** (explosion of a massive star).

**Bright Nebula**

**Dark Nebula**

Use the words in the box to complete the sentences.

| hot | dust | star | dark | telescope | clouds | nebulae |
|-----|------|------|------|-----------|--------|---------|

1. Bright nebulae contain very _____ gases, which make the surrounding cloud glow.

2. The Horsehead Nebula, an interesting _____ nebula, lies within the constellation Orion.

3. Dark nebulae have a lot more _____, which blocks out the light from the stars behind.

4. Scientists believe that nebulae are sites for _____ formation.

5. You need a _____ to see the shape and colors of a nebula.

6. Nebulae are _____ in outer space, made of dust and gases.

7. There are many _____ within spiral and irregular galaxies.

Name _____ Date _____

# Black Holes

OUTER SPACE

**Black holes** were a mysterious discovery in outer space. They are believed to be the remains of a very large star that has collapsed, concentrating its mass into a very small, dense area. The gravitational pull of a black hole is so great that nothing can escape from it, not even light. Scientists have evidence that black holes can capture material from nearby stars. No one knows for sure what happens to the material sucked into a black hole.

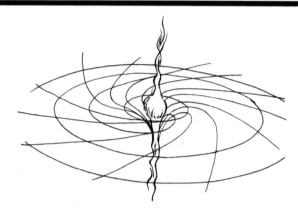

Read each statement. Write **T** if the statement is true or **F** if it is false.

**1** _____ "Dark stars" were predicted by Einstein, but they were not given the name "black holes" until 1967.

**2** _____ The gravitational pull of a black hole is so strong that not even light can escape from it.

**3** _____ Scientists have sent unmanned spaceships into a black hole to gather information.

**4** _____ Black holes form from the collapse of massive stars.

**5** _____ Our sun is big enough to form a black hole.

**6** _____ Scientists have X-ray evidence to show that black holes exist.

**7** _____ Scientists believe black holes distort our perception of time and space, making time slow down.

**8** _____ X-ray pictures of space have shown that black holes can "eat" neighboring stars.

**9** _____ There are black holes the size of stars and some the size of galaxies.

**10** _____ Astronomers have discovered all the black holes that exist in outer space.

Name _____ Date _____

# Life Cycle of Stars

OUTER SPACE

Stars are not all the same. They form inside nebulae. As gravity pulls the gases of the cloud closer together, heat and pressure cause nuclear reactions to begin and a star is born. The type of star formed depends on the amount of material it contains and its temperature. The temperature of a star makes it glow with a particular color. The life cycle of the star also depends on its size. Not all stars follow the same path.

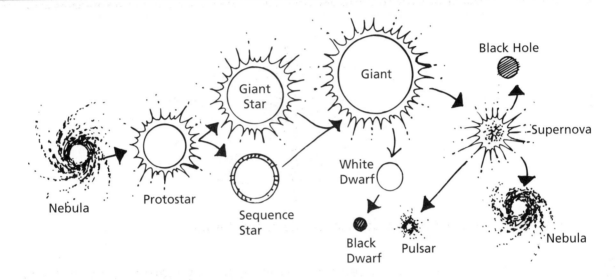

Use the words in the box to complete the sentences.

| yellow | red | orange | white dwarfs | supernova | protostars | pulsar |

**1** Our sun is a main sequence star and glows with a _____ color.

**2** Super giant stars are cooler and glow with a _____ color.

**3** A super giant star can explode as a _____.

**4** Most of the stars we see in the sky at night are main sequence stars or _____.

**5** Giant stars glow with an _____ color.

**6** As the gases in a nebula condense, spinning balls called _____ form.

**7** The core of a supernova may form a small, powerful, spinning star called a _____.

Science • 5–6 © 2005 Creative Teaching Press

Name _____ Date _____

# Outer Space Crossword Puzzle

OUTER SPACE

Write the word that best matches each clue to complete the crossword puzzle.

| | | | | | |
|---|---|---|---|---|---|
| star | universe | pulsar | meteor | moon | red | SOS |
| beam | Mercury | sun | galaxy | go | comet | Venus |
| nebulae | asteroid | solar system | | | | |

**Across**
2. All of outer space
4. Second planet from the sun
6. Enormous system of stars in space
7. Another name for a ray of light bouncing off the moon
9. Spinning remains of a collapsed star
11. Emergency distress signal (abbrev.)
12. Mixture of rock, dust, and frozen gases that travel in an oblong orbit
13. A satellite that orbits a planet
14. A mass of bright, hot gases
15. The planet closest to the sun

**Down**
1. A color of super giant stars
3. All the planets, moons, and space objects that orbit the sun
5. Cloud-like masses of dust and gas
6. Opposite of "stop"
8. Small piece of rocky debris in space
10. Large mass of rock and metal debris
11. Center of our solar system

Name _____ Date _____

# What Are Elements?

CHEMISTRY

**Matter** is anything that takes up space and weighs something (has mass). All matter is made from simple chemical substances known as **elements**. The smallest piece of an element is called an **atom**. There are 92 naturally occurring elements on the earth, plus several man-made ones. Scientists abbreviate the name of an element by writing a chemical symbol, such as H for hydrogen or Cl for chlorine.

| 9 |
|---|
| **C** |
| Carbon |
| 12.0107 |

| 26 |
|---|
| **Fe** |
| Iron |
| 55.845 |

| 16 |
|---|
| **S** |
| Sulfur |
| 32.065 |

| 8 |
|---|
| **O** |
| Oxygen |
| 15.9994 |

| 29 |
|---|
| **Cu** |
| Copper |
| 63.546 |

Read each statement. Write **T** if the statement is true or **F** if it is false.

**1** _____ An element is a substance made of just one kind of atom.

**2** _____ Most of the elements are solids.

**3** _____ Some of the elements are gases.

**4** _____ None of the elements are liquids.

**5** _____ A chemical symbol is usually the first letter of the chemical's name, written as a capital letter.

**6** _____ More than one element can share a chemical symbol.

**7** _____ Some of the symbols come from the Latin names for the elements.

**8** _____ If a symbol is written with two letters, the second letter is always written in lowercase.

**9** _____ Water and salt are examples of elements.

**10** _____ Each element has its own characteristics or properties.

Science • 5–6 © 2005 Creative Teaching Press

Name _____ Date _____

# Structure of Atoms

## CHEMISTRY

**Atoms** are the building blocks of all matter. Each element is composed of a different type of atom. However, all atoms are built from the same three kinds of particles. The center of an atom, called the **nucleus,** contains protons and neutrons. Orbiting around the nucleus in various shells are **electrons.** The number of protons an atom has is called its **atomic number.** This will determine what its properties are like.

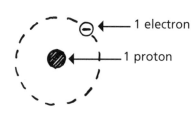
← 1 electron
← 1 proton

**Hydrogen Atom**

13 protons
14 neutrons
13 electrons

**Aluminum Atom**

Match each item to its description.

**1** _____ Nucleus of an atom

**2** _____ Positively charged particles in an atom

**3** _____ Neutral particles in an atom

**4** _____ The number of protons an atom has

**5** _____ Negatively charged particles of an atom

**6** _____ Contains an equal number of protons and electrons

**7** _____ The atomic number determines this

**A.** atomic number

**B.** neutrons

**C.** electrons

**D.** a neutral atom

**E.** contains protons and neutrons

**F.** protons

**G.** properties of the atom

Name _____ Date _____

# Molecules

### CHEMISTRY

> **Molecules** are made of two or more atoms that have combined. Some molecules contain two atoms of the same element, such as an oxygen molecule. However, most molecules are made of combinations of atoms from several elements. These molecules form **chemical compounds** because two or more elements have combined. Most matter exists in the form of molecules.

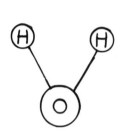

**Water Molecule**

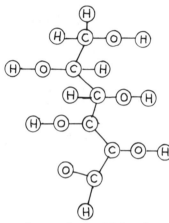

**Oxygen Molecule**

**Brown Sugar Molecule**

Use the words in the box to complete the sentences.

| | | | | | | | |
|---|---|---|---|---|---|---|---|
| solid | liquid | oxygen | gas | temperature | compound | molecules | atoms |

**1** Molecules that contain atoms from several elements form a _____.

**2** Molecules in a _____ are very close together and vibrate in place.

**3** An atom found in all the molecules shown above is _____.

**4** Molecules in a _____ are touching one another but can move about.

**5** Molecules are made of several _____ that have combined.

**6** Molecules in a _____ spread far apart and move very rapidly.

**7** Most of the matter you see, such as water or salt, exists in the form of _____.

**8** If you increase the _____, molecules will move faster.

Name _____ Date _____

# Periodic Table

### Chemistry

All of the elements have been organized into a chart that lets scientists study their similarities and differences. This chart is called the **periodic table,** and it was first devised by a Russian chemistry professor, Dmitri Mendeleev, in 1869. As new elements were discovered, they were added to the periodic table. The elements going down each column have similar properties. More information is given inside each box.

**A Section of the Periodic Table**

| 1 | | | | | | | |
|---|---|---|---|---|---|---|---|
| H | | | | | | | |
| Hydrogen 1.00797 | | | | | | | |

| 3 | 4 |
|---|---|
| Li | Be |
| Lithium 6.941 | Beryllium 9.0122 |

| 11 | 12 |
|---|---|
| Na | Mg |
| Sodium 22.9898 | Magnesium 24.305 |

| 19 | 20 | 21 | 22 | 23 | 24 | 25 | 26 |
|---|---|---|---|---|---|---|---|
| K | Ca | Sc | Ti | V | Cr | Mn | Fe |
| Potassium 39.0983 | Calcium 40.08 | Scandium 44.956 | Titanium 47.88 | Vanadium 50.942 | Chromium 51.996 | Manganese 54.9380 | Iron 55.847 |

| 37 | 38 | 39 | 40 | 41 | 42 | 43 | 44 |
|---|---|---|---|---|---|---|---|
| Rb | Sr | Y | Zr | Nb | Mo | Tc | Ru |
| Rubidium 85.4678 | Strontium 87.62 | Yttrium 88.905 | Zirconium 91.22 | Niobium 92.906 | Molybdenum 95.94 | Technetium (98) | Ruthenium 101.07 |

Use the words in the box to complete the sentences.

| symbol | number | weight | elements | properties | group | period |
|---|---|---|---|---|---|---|

**1** The letters inside each box represent the chemical _____ for the element.

**2** The periodic table organizes all of the _____.

**3** The number above the symbol is the atomic _____ of that element.

**4** The number below the symbol is the atomic _____ of that element.

**5** Each column going down the periodic table is called an atomic _____ and all of these elements have similar _____.

**6** Each row going across the periodic table is called a _____, which shows how a sequence of properties repeats itself, similar to the days of the week.

Science • 5–6 © 2005 Creative Teaching Press

# Chemical Formulas

### CHEMISTRY

**Chemical formulas** are like recipes used for cooking. Formulas tell us which ingredients (elements) are in a compound and the amount of each ingredient that is needed (number of atoms). Chemical formulas are written using the symbols for the elements and small numbers. The small numbers that indicate how many atoms of that element are needed are always written right after the symbol.

| Name of Compound | Formula | Uses |
|---|---|---|
| Water | $H_2O$ | Necessary for all living things |
| Table Sugar | $C_{12}H_{22}O_{11}$ | Cooking, baking, sweetening |
| Calcium Carbonate | $CaCO_3$ | Chalk, cement |
| Baking Soda | $NaHCO_3$ | Baking breads and desserts |
| Vinegar | $HC_2H_3O_2$ | Pickling, salad dressings |

Use the table to complete the statements about chemical formulas.

**1** The elements in water are _____ and _____.

**2** Table sugar contains _____ atoms of carbon, _____ atoms of hydrogen, and _____ atoms of oxygen.

**3** Altogether, there are _____ atoms in a molecule of table sugar.

**4** There are _____ elements in a molecule of baking soda.

**5** There are a total of _____ atoms in a molecule of baking soda.

**6** In a molecule of vinegar, there are a total of _____ hydrogen atoms.

**7** How many elements are needed to make a molecule of vinegar? _____

Name _____ Date _____

# Changes of State

## CHEMISTRY

Matter exists as a solid, liquid, or gas. A change in temperature can cause a change of state. When you increase the temperature, the molecules begin to move more rapidly. This is what allows a solid to melt or a liquid to boil. Lowering the temperature makes the molecules slow down. This happens when gases condense into liquids, or when liquids freeze. The matter is still the same kind of matter it was before.

| Type of Matter | Normal State | Alternate State |
|---|---|---|
| Table Sugar | Solid | Liquid (simple syrup) |
| Water | Liquid | Solid–Ice<br>Gas–Water Vapor |
| Oxygen | Gas | Liquid<br>(rocket fuel systems) |
| Carbon Dioxide | Gas | Solid–Dry Ice |

Use the table to complete the statements.

**1** Changes of state are a result of a change in the _____ of the matter.

**2** If table sugar is heated gently, it will change from a _____ to a _____.

**3** Which substance in the table is commonly found in all three states of matter? _____

**4** Dry ice is frozen _____. When exposed to room temperature, it changes directly into a _____ by a process called sublimation.

**5** Oxygen makes up about 20% of the air in the form of a _____.

**6** Oxygen is used in some rocket fuel systems. To change oxygen to a _____, it must be cooled to a temperature of –297.3°F (–183°C).

Name _____ Date _____

# Density of Matter

## CHEMISTRY

**Density** is a property of matter that describes how heavy it is for its size. Density compares the weight of matter to its volume. In some types of matter, the molecules are more closely packed together. These materials have a higher density. Scientists compare everything to water, which is given a density of one. Matter with a density of less than one will float. Matter with a density greater than one will sink.

Why does a paper clip sink and a big ocean liner float? Explain your answer.

_____

_____

_____

_____

_____

_____

_____

_____

Name _____ Date _____

# Physical Properties of Matter

### Chemistry

> **Physical properties** are the characteristics of matter that we can determine by using our five senses. They include the state of matter and its shape, size, color, taste, and texture, among other things. They are all inherent characteristics of the matter and do not involve changing the matter into a different substance. Physical properties help scientists determine what the matter can be used for.

Put a ✓ by all the things that are physical properties of matter.

**1** _____ The state of the matter

**2** _____ The shape of the piece of matter

**3** _____ The density of the matter

**4** _____ The ability of some matter to burn

**5** _____ The hardness of the matter

**6** _____ The ability of some matter to dissolve in water

**7** _____ The fact that some matter is poisonous

**8** _____ The ability of some matter to conduct electricity

**9** _____ The ability of matter to react with other chemicals

**10** _____ The odor of the matter

*Science • 5–6 © 2005 Creative Teaching Press*

Name _____ Date _____

# Metals vs. Nonmetals

### Chemistry

Eighty-five percent of all the elements are metals. Metals are substances that have a shiny surface. This is called a **metallic luster.** Nonmetals look dull. Almost all metals are solids at room temperature. Nonmetals can be solids, liquids, or gases. Nonmetals tend to be located on the right side of the periodic table.

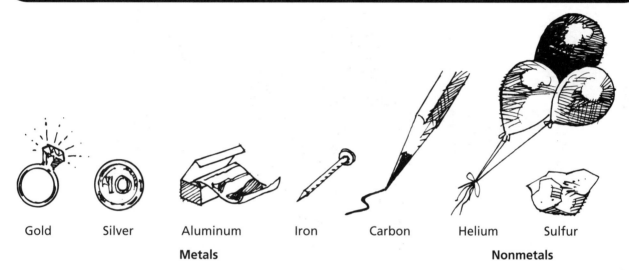

| Gold | Silver | Aluminum | Iron | Carbon | Helium | Sulfur |

**Metals**                                    **Nonmetals**

Write **M** if the sentence describes metals or **N** if it describes nonmetals.

**1** _____ Most of these are silver to gray in color.

**2** _____ These substances easily break into pieces when hammered.

**3** _____ Most of these are good conductors of heat and electricity.

**4** _____ Almost all of these are solids at room temperature.

**5** _____ These can be hammered into different shapes without breaking.

**6** _____ These substances come in many colors.

**7** _____ Many of these can be formed into thin wires.

**8** _____ These elements can be solids, liquids, or gases.

**9** _____ The majority of elements belong to this group.

**10** _____ Carbon, oxygen, sulfur, and neon belong to this group.

Name _____ Date _____

# Dissolving in Water

CHEMISTRY

When you mix a substance with water, it may seem to disappear. It didn't really disappear; it just dissolved in the water. Chemicals that dissolve in water separate into individual molecules, fitting in between the water molecules. The molecules are evenly distributed among all the water molecules. This forms a type of mixture called a **solution.** Things that dissolve are called **soluble;** things that do not are called **insoluble.**

Water Molecules

● = Salt molecules

○ = Water molecules

A Salt Solution

Read each statement. Write **T** if the statement is true or **F** if it is false.

**1** _____ Water is called the universal solvent because so many things dissolve in water.

**2** _____ When something dissolves in water, the water should look transparent.

**3** _____ Lowering the temperature of the water helps substances to dissolve faster.

**4** _____ You can often dissolve another liquid in water.

**5** _____ Gases do not dissolve in water.

**6** _____ A concentrated solution is one that has a lot of the chemical dissolved in the water.

**7** _____ A saturated solution has as much as possible dissolved in the water.

**8** _____ The substance that dissolves in the water is called the solvent.

**9** _____ Solutions can have a color.

**10** _____ When a substance dissolves in water, its molecules spread out evenly between the water molecules.

*Science • 5–6 © 2005 Creative Teaching Press*

Name _____ Date _____

# Solutions and Suspensions

## Chemistry

Solutions and suspensions are both types of mixtures. Two or more substances have been mixed together, but they still retain all their own properties. In a **solution,** all of the substance dissolves and you can see clearly through it. In a **suspension,** there are very tiny particles or droplets, often too small to see, which are evenly distributed throughout the mixture. They do not settle out, but they do stay suspended in the mixture.

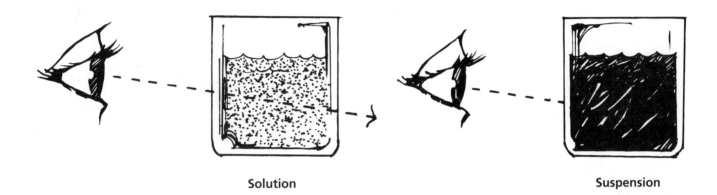

**Solution**                    **Suspension**

Write **S** if the sentence describes a solution, **P** if it describes a suspension, or **B** if it describes both solutions and suspensions.

**1** _____ A cup of tea is an example of this.

**2** _____ Milk is an example of this.

**3** _____ Fog and clouds are examples of this.

**4** _____ Blood is an example of this.

**5** _____ All of the ingredients still retain their properties.

**6** _____ Mayonnaise is an example of this.

**7** _____ This is a type of mixture.

**8** _____ Everything is dissolved in this one.

**9** _____ You can see clearly through this one.

**10** _____ You cannot see clearly through this one.

Name _____ Date _____

# Mixtures vs. Compounds

### CHEMISTRY

Everything that is considered matter is an element, a mixture, or a compound. Mixtures and compounds are much more common than pure elements. In a **mixture,** the parts are just mixed together, not combined. Each substance retains its own properties. A **compound** is made of two or more elements that have chemically combined. They make something new, with new and different properties.

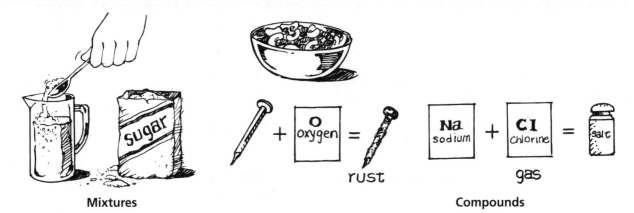

**Mixtures**                                                    **Compounds**

Write each characteristic listed in the box under the correct heading.

| | | |
|---|---|---|
| Made up of elements | Not chemically combined | Parts cannot be easily separated |
| Retains original properties | Chemically combined | Has a formula |
| Parts can be separated by physical methods | | Cannot write a formula |
| Has new and different properties | | Made of compounds, elements, or both |

**Mixtures**                                                    **Compounds**

_____          _____

_____          _____

_____          _____

_____          _____

_____          _____

Name _____ Date _____

# Chemical Properties of Matter

## CHEMISTRY

**Chemical properties** are characteristics that you cannot identify just by looking at a substance. You have to do a chemical test or experiment to determine the chemical properties of a substance. Chemical properties concern the tendency of a substance to change into something different. Some chemicals react with other chemicals very easily, while others are less active, or even inert.

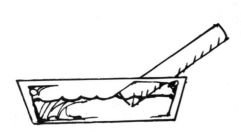

Testing for acids and bases with litmus paper.

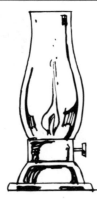

Kerosine in a lantern will burn.

Put a ✓ by the sentences that describe chemical properties of matter.

**1** _____ Some substances are acids, which can be identified by testing with litmus paper.

**2** _____ Fuels have the ability to burn in the presence of oxygen.

**3** _____ Salt can dissolve in water.

**4** _____ Acids and bases react together to produce neutral salts.

**5** _____ Metals release hydrogen gas in the presence of an acid.

**6** _____ Alka-Seltzer® tablets fizz when placed in water.

**7** _____ Butter melts when left out on a table on a warm day.

**8** _____ Neon gas is inert and doesn't react with other chemicals.

**9** _____ Moist iron will rust in the presence of oxygen.

**10** _____ You can change the density of water by adding salt to it.

Name _____ Date _____

# Chemical Changes

In a **chemical change,** the chemical properties of the substance change. Chemical changes always involve creating different matter, with different properties than the original components you started with. Energy is either needed or released when a chemical change occurs. There are three main types of chemical changes: **combination reactions, decomposition reactions,** and **replacement reactions.**

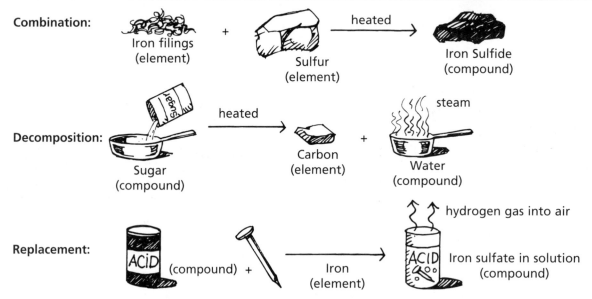

Write **C** if the sentence describes a combination reaction, **D** if it describes a decomposition reaction, or **R** if it describes a replacement reaction.

**1** _____ Two elements join to create a compound.

**2** _____ Part of a compound is replaced by part of another compound.

**3** _____ A compound is made to break apart into simpler substances.

**4** _____ Steel wool (iron) is burned in the presence of oxygen in the air and makes iron oxide.

**5** _____ Hydrogen peroxide ($H_2O_2$) fizzes on human skin and releases oxygen (which kills germs) and water.

**6** _____ An iron nail placed in sulfuric acid ($H_2SO_4$) releases hydrogen gas and creates iron sulfate.

**7** _____ Part of a compound is replaced by a different element.

*Science • 5–6* © 2005 Creative Teaching Press

Name _____ Date _____

# Physical or Chemical Change?

CHEMISTRY

To determine if a change is a physical or chemical change, ask yourself if anything new was created or if the properties of the substance have been changed. If so, it is a chemical change. Remember, physical changes do not change the matter into a new and different kind. Physical changes only change the physical properties.

**Physical Change**

**Chemical Change**

Write **P** if the sentence describes a physical change or **C** if it describes a chemical change.

**1** _____ A rock is chopped up into small pebbles.

**2** _____ Cake mix, water, eggs, and oil are baked into a cake.

**3** _____ Oil and water are shaken together to make salad dressing.

**4** _____ A glass is dropped and broken.

**5** _____ Water is put into the freezer to make ice.

**6** _____ We use detergent and bleach to wash clothes and remove stains.

**7** _____ Your mother cooks some scrambled eggs.

**8** _____ Modeling clay is shaped into a vase.

**9** _____ Cream is whipped with air to make whipped cream.

**10** _____ Gasoline is burned in a car's engine.

# Chemistry Word Scramble

### CHEMISTRY

Unscramble the words and complete the definitions.

**1** EEELMNT _____: one of 92 naturally occurring pure substances, made only of itself

**2** EUCLOMEL _____: two or more atoms combined

**3** DNUOPMOC _____: two or more elements combined

**4** SITROPRPEE _____: the physical and chemical characteristics of matter

**5** MTOA _____: the smallest piece of an element

**6** TREAMT _____: anything that takes up space and has weight (mass)

**7** TMECHISYR _____: the study of matter and its properties

**8** OSLTIOUN _____: a type of mixture where the ingredients are dissolved

**9** CLEUUNS _____: the center of the atom where protons and neutrons are located

**10** LCRNTEEOS _____: the negatively charged particles in an atom.

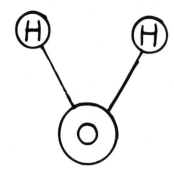
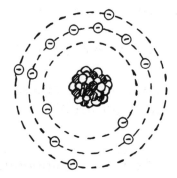

Name _____  Date _____

# Heat Energy

### Light and Heat

All matter contains thermal energy from the movement of its atoms and molecules. This movement creates heat. The faster the molecules move, the greater the quantity of heat that is produced. Heat always moves from a warmer object to a cooler object. Sometimes the heat released or absorbed from an object allows the material to change its state. It may freeze, melt, evaporate, or condense.

| Object | Melting Point |
|---|---|
| Ice | 32°F (0°C) |
| Candle Wax | 120–160°F (49–71°C) |
| Lead | 621.7°F (327.6°C) |
| Gold | 1948°F (1064.43°C) |
| Copper | 1981.4°F (1083°C) |
| Iron | 2795°F (1535°C) |

Use the words in the box to complete the sentences.

| | | | | | | | |
|---|---|---|---|---|---|---|---|
| freeze | warmer | colder | evaporate | melt | candle wax | lead | iron |

**1** Heat always moves from a _____ object to a _____ object.

**2** If a liquid absorbs enough heat, it will _____.

**3** When water reaches 32°F (0°C), it will begin to _____.

**4** When ice reaches 32°F (0°C), it will begin to _____.

**5** Copper melts at a higher temperature than _____, which makes it a stronger metal.

**6** _____ melts over a range of temperatures because it is a mixture of different compounds.

**7** The element _____ is very strong, partly because it has a very high melting point.

Name _____ Date _____

# Sources of Heat

### Light and Heat

The sun is our main source of heat. The land, water, and air all absorb heat from the sun. Other sources of heat include friction, electricity, burning fuels, nuclear reactions, percussion, and chemical reactions within living organisms. Heat may be a desired product, as in electric heaters and the burning of fuels. Other times, heat is undesirable, like that caused by friction from machines.

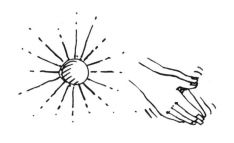    

| **Sun** | **Friction** | **Electricity** | **Burning Fuels** | **Nuclear Reactions** | **Percussion** |

Match the heat produced to its source.

**1** _____ Heat caused by resistance in the wires

**2** _____ Heat from objects rubbing against each other

**3** _____ Heat produced by moving molecules in matter

**4** _____ Light is converted to heat energy by opaque objects

**5** _____ Heat produced from striking an object

**6** _____ Heat produced from fusing or splitting atoms

**7** _____ Stored chemical energy released as heat

**A.** nuclear reactions

**B.** electricity

**C.** percussion

**D.** from burning fuels and in living organisms

**E.** friction

**F.** thermal energy

**G.** sunlight

# Heat Conduction

### LIGHT AND HEAT

Heat travels through solids by **conduction**. A hot flame makes the molecules in the tip of a nail begin to get hot. As this happens, the molecules in the nail begin to move faster. They vibrate in place. They bump into the molecules next to them. The fast-moving molecules make the other molecules move faster. Heat energy is passed from molecule to molecule, but the matter itself does not move from its place.

Read each statement. Write **T** if the statement is true or **F** if it is false.

**1** _____ Heat travels by conduction when the molecules stop moving around.

**2** _____ Heat travels through solids by conduction.

**3** _____ Snow is a good conductor of heat.

**4** _____ All solids do not conduct heat at the same rate.

**5** _____ As molecules get hotter, they move faster.

**6** _____ In conduction, heat energy is passed through matter, but the matter itself does not move.

**7** _____ You could see the heat being conducted through the nail in the picture above.

**8** _____ You could feel the heat being conducted through the nail in the picture above.

Name _____ Date _____

# Heat Conductors and Insulators

### Light and Heat

Some materials are better conductors than others. If you stand barefooted on the tile floor of a bathroom in the morning, it may feel cool to your feet. After a few minutes, it doesn't feel so cold. The heat from your feet traveled by conduction into the tile, balancing out the temperature of both. We use good heat conductors for cooking pots and pans. Poor conductors are called **insulators.** They slow the flow of heat.

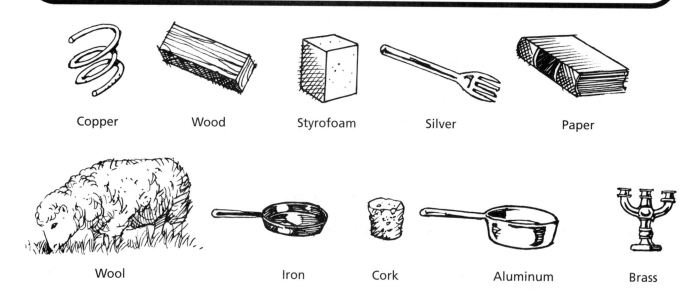

| Copper | Wood | Styrofoam | Silver | Paper |

| Wool | Iron | Cork | Aluminum | Brass |

Sort the objects into **Conductors** and **Insulators** of heat.

| **Conductors** | **Insulators** |
| --- | --- |
| _____ | _____ |
| _____ | _____ |
| _____ | _____ |
| _____ | _____ |
| _____ | _____ |

*Science • 5–6 © 2005 Creative Teaching Press*

Name _____ Date _____

# Expansion and Contraction

### LIGHT AND HEAT

> When materials are heated they tend to expand. Their molecules are moving faster and they move a little farther apart. This makes the object a little larger. When matter is cooled it contracts. The molecules are moving more slowly and they move a little closer together. Now the object is a little smaller. This happens with solids, liquids, and gases. The expansion and contraction of gases is the most dramatic.

  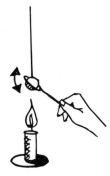 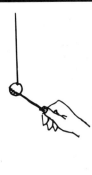

**A Gas Heating**          **A Gas Cooling**          **A Solid Heating**          **A Solid Cooling**

Read each statement. Write **T** if the statement is true or **F** if it is false.

**1** _____ The cracks between sections of a concrete sidewalk allow for expansion and contraction.

**2** _____ Water contracts as it gets colder until it reaches 39°F (4°C), and then it expands as it freezes.

**3** _____ Solids contract and expand more easily than gases.

**4** _____ It is easier to open a tight-fitting metal lid on a jar after running it under hot water.

**5** _____ A balloon filled with warm air will expand as it cools.

**6** _____ Hot water may boil over the edges of a pot due to expansion.

**7** _____ Expansion is due to the increased movement of molecules in matter.

**8** _____ The molecules in an object get smaller as it contracts.

**9** _____ Not all solids expand and contract at the same rate.

**10** _____ Thermometers contain liquids that expand as the weather gets hotter.

# Convection and Radiation

### LIGHT AND HEAT

Heat travels through liquids and gases by **convection.** As the molecules get hotter, they begin to move more rapidly. This movement sets up currents in the liquid or gas. The warmer molecules rise and the cooler molecules sink. This is what causes wind and ocean currents. Radiation doesn't require the movement of molecules. **Radiation** is the release of heat energy waves, which can travel through outer space.

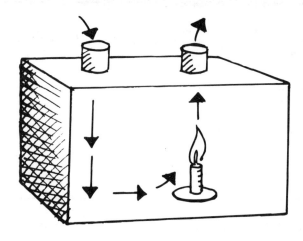

**Convection Current**

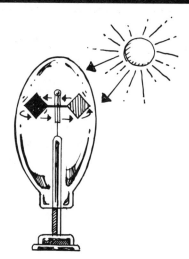

**Radiation from the sun**

Use the words in the box to complete the sentences.

| convection | wind | sun | ocean | molecules | outer space | radiate | within |
|---|---|---|---|---|---|---|---|

**1** Heat from our closest star, the _____, travels by radiation.

**2** Heat travels through liquids and gases by _____.

**3** Convection currents in the _____ and _____ rely on the movement of _____ to transfer heat from one place to another.

**4** The heat from a campfire can _____ outward and warm us up.

**5** The sun is 93 million miles away, but its heat can travel through _____.

**6** Convection currents also exist _____ the earth's mantle.

Science • 5–6 © 2005 Creative Teaching Press

Name _____ Date _____

# Electromagnetic Spectrum

## Light and Heat

There is a wide range of energy waves that make up what is called the **electromagnetic spectrum.** Most of these are invisible to the human eye. They all travel at the same speed, but they vary in their wavelength and frequency. Think of two people holding a long jump rope. One person can move the rope up and down, fast or slow. The bumpiness of the rope can change, just as the frequency of these waves changes.

| Radio Waves | Infrared | **Visible Light** | Ultraviolet | X-rays | Gamma Rays | Cosmic Rays |
|---|---|---|---|---|---|---|

**Lower Frequency**                                                                    **Higher Frequency**

Read each statement. Write **T** if the statement is true or **F** if it is false.

**1** _____ The frequency refers to the number of cycles, or bumps, an energy wave makes in a second.

**2** _____ Radio waves are used for heating and cooking.

**3** _____ Infrared waves are heat energy waves.

**4** _____ Visible light is the part of the spectrum that humans can see.

**5** _____ Ultraviolet has a lower frequency than visible light.

**6** _____ X-ray energy waves can pass through the human body.

**7** _____ Gamma rays have a high frequency and are used for treating cancer.

**8** _____ As the frequency of an energy wave increases, so does its wavelength.

**9** _____ The electromagnetic spectrum does not include sound waves.

**10** _____ The wavelength is the distance it takes for an energy wave to make one cycle.

Name _____ Date _____

# Infrared and Microwaves

### LIGHT AND HEAT

**Infrared waves** are invisible but are felt as heat. **Microwaves** are lower frequency radio waves. They're invisible, too. Infrared waves make molecules move and matter get hot. Microwaves can penetrate only certain things. They make water, fat, and sugar molecules move so much that the heat actually "cooks" food. Microwaves are not absorbed by most plastic, glass, or ceramics. Metals reflect microwaves.

**Heat Lamp**

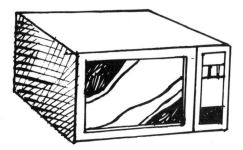

**Microwave Oven**

Use the words in the box to complete the sentences.

| warm | invisible | heat | molecules | food | metal | energy | glow |
|------|-----------|------|-----------|------|-------|--------|------|

**1** Both infrared and microwaves are types of _____ waves.

**2** Infrared heat lamps are used in fast-food restaurants to keep food _____ until it's served.

**3** A hot charcoal grill will emit infrared waves as well as some visible light, making the coals _____.

**4** Infrared and microwaves are _____ to the human eye.

**5** Microwaves can penetrate the water, fat, and sugar molecules found in _____.

**6** Infrared and microwaves make the _____ of the matter move.

**7** We feel infrared waves as _____.

**8** You should never put _____ in a microwave oven because it reflects the microwaves.

*Science • 5–6* © 2005 Creative Teaching Press

Name _____ Date _____

# Sunlight and Blue Sky

LIGHT AND HEAT

**Sunlight** includes all the colors of visible light, some infrared, and some ultraviolet light. As light from the sun passes through the atmosphere, the blue-violet part of the spectrum gets more scattered. Our eyes are more sensitive to light with blue frequencies, so the sky appears blue. The less dust and water vapor there is in the air, the deeper blue the sky becomes.

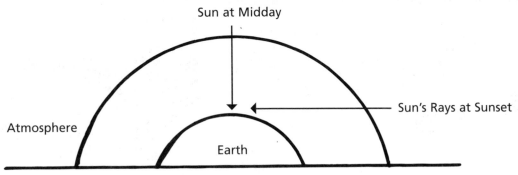

Sunlight passes through the atmosphere.

Read each statement. Write **T** if the statement is true or **F** if it is false.

**1** _____ Sunlight is made only of visible light.

**2** _____ Visible light contains all the colors of the rainbow.

**3** _____ All the colors of visible light mixed together appear as white light to our eyes.

**4** _____ Light waves from the sun bump into the molecules of air in the atmosphere.

**5** _____ In the middle of the day, sunlight travels a longer distance through the atmosphere.

**6** _____ The atmosphere scatters blue to violet light the most.

**7** _____ Air that contains a lot of dust or water vapor scatters less blue light, making the sky look pale.

**8** _____ The angle of the light at sunrise and sunset causes more red to orange light to reach our eyes.

**9** _____ You can see ultraviolet light.

**10** _____ The sky looks blue because the earth's surface reflects blue light back up into the atmosphere.

Name _____  Date _____

# Ultraviolet Light

### LIGHT AND HEAT

You cannot see ultraviolet light, but it is part of sunlight. **Ultraviolet light** can penetrate the upper part of your skin and cause a tan or sunburn. Exposure to too much ultraviolet light can cause skin cancer. Some insects can see the ultraviolet light emitted by certain flowers and are attracted by it. Fluorescent paint, some minerals, and "black light" posters glow in ultraviolet light.

Use the words in the box to complete the sentences.

| |
|---|
| window<br>butterflies<br>sunburn<br>wrinkles<br>cancer<br>disinfect<br>invisible<br>black |

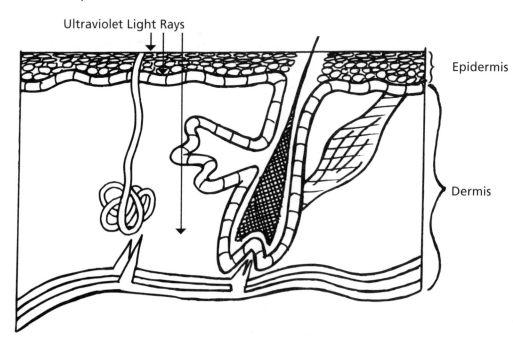

Ultraviolet Light Rays

Epidermis

Dermis

**1** Ultraviolet light is _____ to the human eye.

**2** Some insects, including flies and _____ are attracted to ultraviolet light.

**3** Ultraviolet light can penetrate the epidermis of the skin, causing a _____ after a short, intense exposure.

**4** Exposure to ultraviolet light over many years increases the formation of _____ and can cause skin _____.

**5** Ultraviolet light cannot penetrate _____ glass.

**6** Ultraviolet light can kill germs and is also used to _____ water.

**7** Fluorescent paint and some minerals glow when exposed to ultraviolet light, also called _____ light.

Science • 5–6 © 2005 Creative Teaching Press

Name _____ Date _____

# Fiber Optics

### Light and Heat

Fiber optic cables are like bundles of miniature straws. Light is reflected back and forth inside the hollow tube of very thin optical fibers. Optical fibers can be used to transmit information the same way that electricity is used in computers and telephone lines. They are even more efficient than electricity and have no fire danger. Fiber optic cables can also be safely used inside the body in diagnostic instruments.

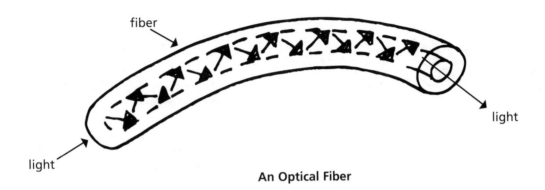

fiber

light

light

**An Optical Fiber**

Read each statement. Write **T** if the statement is true or **F** if it is false.

**1** _____ Optical fibers as thin as human hair carry hundreds of telephone conversations at the same time.

**2** _____ A fiber optic cable is made of bundles of thin optical fibers.

**3** _____ Optical fibers must be insulated to keep the light inside.

**4** _____ Fiber optics can be used to transmit computer data.

**5** _____ You can get a shock from touching fiber optic cables.

**6** _____ Fiber optic cables are used in instruments for medical diagnosis and research.

**7** _____ Light travels down an optical fiber by reflecting back and forth.

**8** _____ Currently, the main drawback of optical fibers is that they are rather expensive to use.

**9** _____ Optical fibers get hot the same way electrical wires do.

**10** _____ We will probably find more uses for optical fibers in the future.

Science • 5–6 © 2005 Creative Teaching Press

Name _____ Date _____

# Lasers

### LIGHT AND HEAT

> **Laser light** is different from ordinary light. Regular light, or white light, contains all the colors of visible light. Laser light is all the same frequency. The light energy in a laser is very concentrated, but it can be controlled very precisely. Lasers can cut through steel, but they are also used for delicate eye surgery. Laser light is also used to produce 3-D photographic pictures called **holograms**.

**Ordinary Light**

**Laser Light**

Put a ✓ by all the sentences that accurately describe laser light.

**1** _____ Laser light is made of a mixture of frequencies.

**2** _____ Mirrors are placed at each end of the laser tube to concentrate the light.

**3** _____ Lasers are found in grocery store scanners.

**4** _____ Lasers are powerful enough to burn through metal.

**5** _____ To make holograms, laser light is split into two beams and reflected onto film at different angles.

**6** _____ Lasers do not require an outside energy source to create the laser light.

**7** _____ Lasers can be safely used for delicate eye surgery.

**8** _____ You need to wear special 3-D glasses to view holograms.

**9** _____ Laser light has less energy than ordinary light.

**10** _____ Rubies or carbon dioxide are often used as the source for energy absorption and laser emission.

*Science • 5–6 © 2005 Creative Teaching Press*

# Answer Key

## Human Skeleton (page 5)

1. J
2. D
3. I
4. B
5. C
6. E
7. H
8. G
9. A
10. F

## Types of Joints (page 6)

1. skull
2. shoulder, hip
3. wrist, neck
4. backbone
5. knee, elbow
6. wrist, neck, ankle

## The Brain (page 7)

1. medulla
2. cerebrum
3. cerebellum
4. medulla
5. cerebrum
6. medulla
7. cerebellum
8. cerebrum
9. cerebellum
10. cerebrum

## The Nervous System (page 8)

1. T
2. F
3. T
4. T
5. T
6. T
7. F
8. T
9. T
10. T

## The Heart (page 9)

1. blood
2. valves
3. lungs
4. body
5. ventricles
6. receive
7. pump
8. auricles

## Your Blood (page 10)

1. T
2. F
3. T
4. T
5. T
6. F
7. T
8. F
9. T
10. T

## What Are Carbohydrates and Fats? (page 11)

1. C
2. C
3. F
4. C
5. F
6. F
7. C
8. F

## What Are Proteins? (page 12)

Put a ✔ by 2, 3, 4, 5, 7, and 8.

## Digestion (page 13)

The correct order is 1, 3, 2, 5, 4, 6.

## Vitamins (page 14)

1. milk
2. K
3. D
4. C
5. A
6. $B_2$

## Minerals We Eat (page 15)

1. E
2. B
3. G
4. D
5. H
6. C
7. A
8. F

## A Balanced Diet (page 16)

1. missing fruit group
2. missing meat group
3. missing dairy group

Circle candy, soda, donut, jelly, catsup, fruit roll, and chips.

## Your Lungs (page 17)

1. T
2. T
3. T
4. F
5. T
6. F
7. T
8. F
9. T
10. T

## The Excretory System (page 18)

1. kidney
2. bladder
3. ureter
4. minerals
5. protein
6. urethra
7. water

## Muscles at Work (page 19)

1. skeletal
2. smooth
3. cardiac
4. smooth
5. smooth
6. smooth
7. skeletal
8. skeletal
9. skeletal

## The Skin (page 20)

1. C
2. G
3. A
4. H
5. D
6. F
7. E
8. B

## Human Body Crossword Puzzle (page 21)

**Across**

1. esophagus
3. liver
4. ligaments
5. kidney
7. tendon
8. tissue
10. bones
11. heart

**Down**

2. lungs
6. muscles
7. teeth
9. organ
12. intestines

## Contagious Diseases (page 22)

1. T
2. F
3. T
4. F
5. T
6. F
7. T
8. T
9. T

## Noncontagious Diseases (page 23)

Put a ✔ by 1, 2, 4, 5, 6, and 8.

## Seed Plants (page 24)

1. A
2. B
3. G
4. A
5. B
6. G
7. A
8. G
9. B

## Flowering Plants (page 25)

1. deciduous
2. fibrous
3. tap
4. woody
5. soft-stemmed
6. monocots
7. dicots

## Pollination and Fertilization (page 26)

1. F
2. T
3. T
4. T
5. F
6. T
7. F
8. F
9. T
10. T

## Conifers (page 27)

Put a ✔ by 1, 3, 4, 5, 7, and 8.

## Photosynthesis (page 28)

1. T
2. T
3. F
4. T
5. F
6. F
7. T
8. T
9. T
10. T

## How Plants Package Seeds (page 29)

**Seed Pods:** green peas, string beans, soybeans, black-eyed peas, pinto beans
**Fleshy Fruits:** orange, apple, watermelon, tomato, cucumber
**Dry Fruits:** wheat, pecan, sunflower, oats, acorn

## Plant Word Scramble (page 30)

1. photosynthesis
2. angiosperms
3. stamen
4. gymnosperms
5. pistil
6. oxygen
7. chlorophyll
8. pollination
9. conifer
10. leaves

## Ferns and Mosses (page 31)

1. B
2. M
3. F
4. B
5. M
6. F
7. F
8. M

### Algae (page 32)

1. chlorophyll
2. plants
3. microscopic
4. seaweed
5. kelp
6. scum
7. food

### Ecosystems (page 33)

1. R
2. S
3. T
4. C
5. S
6. T

### Nature's Decomposers (page 34)

Put a ✔ by 1, 4, 5, 6, and 7.

### Habitat vs. Niche (page 35)

1. T
2. T
3. F
4. T
5. T
6. T
7. F

### Food Webs (page 36)

1. predators
2. bacteria
3. producers
4. seals, killer whales
5. baleen whales, squid

### Harmful Symbiotic Relationships (page 37)

Put a ✔ by 1, 3, 4, 5, and 8.

### Helpful Symbiotic Relationships (page 38)

1. protozoa
2. sea anemone
3. cleaner fish
4. cactus
5. sea slugs
6. lichen
7. moth

### Ecosystems Recycle Chemicals (page 39)

1. F
2. T
3. T
4. T
5. T
6. F
7. T
8. T
9. T
10. F

### Renewable Resources (page 40)

1. renewable
2. wood
3. sun, wind
4. water
5. expand
6. electricity

### Nonrenewable Resources (page 41)

1. industrial
2. residential, transportation
3. coal
4. oil
5. oil
6. residential, commercial

## Coal (page 42)

1. T
2. F
3. T
4. T
5. T
6. T
7. F
8. T
9. T
10. T

## Oil and Natural Gas (page 43)

1. B
2. G
3. O
4. G
5. G
6. O
7. B
8. O
9. B
10. G

## Geothermal Energy (page 44)

Put a ✓ by 1, 4, 5, 6, 7, and 10.

## Wind Energy (page 45)

1. A
2. A
3. D
4. A
5. D
6. D
7. D
8. A
9. A
10. A

## Solar and Nuclear Energy (page 46)

1. B
2. S
3. N
4. S
5. S
6. N
7. B
8. N
9. S
10. B

## Air Pollution (page 47)

1. T
2. T
3. T
4. T
5. F
6. F
7. T
8. T
9. T
10. F

## Clean Drinking Water (page 48)

The correct order is 6, 1, 4, 2, 7, 5, 3.

## Pollution Puzzle (page 49)

1. ground
2. fertilizer
3. outflow
4. unlawful
5. carbon
6. dioxide
7. sewage
8. drains
9. pesticides
10. litter
11. runoff     The key word is GROUNDWATER.

## Plate Tectonics (page 50)

1. crust
2. colliding
3. sliding
4. spreading
5. subducts
6. plates, mantle

## Earthquakes (page 51)

1. T
2. T
3. T
4. F
5. T
6. T
7. F
8. T
9. T
10. F

## Where Do Earthquakes Happen? (page 52)

1. New England
2. Hawaii and Florida
3. Alaska
4. South Carolina
5. Utah

## Types of Volcanoes (page 53)

1. C
2. S
3. C
4. S
5. A
6. A
7. C
8. S
9. A

## Moving Magma in the Mantle (page 54)

1. T
2. T
3. F
4. F
5. T
6. F
7. T
8. T
9. T
10. T

## Faulting and Folding (page 55)

1. tension
2. shear
3. compression
4. flexible
5. brittle
6. temperature, composition

## Water Shapes the Land (page 56)

1. B
2. G
3. H
4. A
5. I
6. D
7. F
8. C
9. E

## Glaciers (page 57)

The correct order is 5, 1, 6, 2, 7, 3, 4.

## Soil Formation (page 58)

1. T
2. S
3. H
4. B
5. T
6. B
7. S

## Types of Soil (page 59)

1. T
2. T
3. F
4. T
5. T
6. F
7. T
8. T
9. F
10. T

## The Earth's Atmosphere (page 60)

1. T
2. M
3. I
4. T
5. S
6. E
7. S
8. I
9. E

## What Causes the Weather? (page 61)

1. T
2. T
3. F
4. F
5. T
6. T
7. T
8. T
9. F
10. F

## Convection Currents in the Air (page 62)

1. faster
2. rises, sink
3. poles
4. convection
5. rotation
6. wind
7. equator

## Land and Sea Breezes (page 63)

1. T
2. F
3. T
4. T
5. F
6. T
7. T
8. T
9. T
10. F

## Air Pressure (page 64)

1. sea level
2. high
3. low
4. barometer
5. better
6. worse
7. air pressure
8. lower

## Humidity (page 65)

1. T
2. F
3. T
4. T
5. T
6. T
7. F
8. F
9. T
10. T

## Precipitation (page 66)

1. C
2. D
3. A
4. E
5. B
6. G
7. F
8. H

## Reading the Clouds (page 67)

1. G
2. A
3. B
4. E
5. D
6. C
7. F

## Cold Fronts (page 68)

Put a ✔ by 2, 4, 5, 6, 7, and 10.

## Warm Fronts (page 69)

Put a ✔ by 1, 2, 4, 5, 6, 9, and 10.

## Thunderstorms (page 70)

1. hours
2. cumulonimbus
3. static
4. warm
5. lightning
6. thunder
7. rain
8. hail

## Hurricanes (page 71)

1. T
2. T
3. F
4. T
5. F
6. T
7. F
8. T
9. T
10. T

## Tornadoes (page 72)

Put a ✔ by 1, 3, 5, 6, 7, 8, and 9.

## Reading Weather Maps (page 73)

1. Miami
2. ◑
3. Denver, Richmond
4. Phoenix
5. wind (tell speed and direction)
6. air pressure
7. 32°F, partly cloudy, blowing 38-43 mph

## Weather Words Rebus Puzzle (page 74)

1. stratus
2. cumulus
3. cirrus
4. evaporate
5. ocean
6. air
7. pressure
8. frost

## The Solar System and the Universe (page 75)

1. universe
2. galaxy
3. solar system
4. sun
5. Jupiter
6. Saturn
7. Earth
8. Earth's moon
9. Pluto

## The Sun (page 76)

1. C
2. F
3. E
4. G
5. B
6. H
7. D
8. A
9. I

## The Moon and the Tides (page 77)

1. tide
2. moon
3. sun
4. high
5. low
6. twice
7. opposite

## Phases of the Moon (page 78)

1. T
2. T
3. T
4. T
5. F
6. T
7. T
8. F
9. F
10. T

## Galaxies (page 79)

1. I
2. S
3. E
4. S
5. I
6. E
7. S

## Zodiac Constellations (page 80)

1. imagined
2. easy
3. not easy
4. astrologers
5. astronomers
6. zodiac

## Comets (page 81)

Put a ✓ by 2, 4, 5, 6, 7, 8, and 10.

## Meteors and Asteroids (page 82)

1. M
2. B
3. B
4. A
5. M
6. M
7. B
8. A
9. A
10. A

## Nebulae (page 83)

1. hot
2. dark
3. dust
4. star
5. telescope
6. clouds
7. nebulae

## Black Holes (page 84)

1. T
2. T
3. F
4. T
5. F
6. T
7. T
8. T
9. T
10. F

## Life Cycle of Stars (page 85)

1. yellow
2. red
3. supernova
4. white dwarfs
5. orange
6. protostars
7. pulsar

## Outer Space Crossword Puzzle (page 86)

**Across**

2. universe
4. Venus
6. galaxy
7. beam
9. pulsar
11. SOS
12. comet
13. moon
14. star
15. Mercury

**Down**

1. red
3. solar system
5. nebulae
6. go
8. meteor
10. asteroid
11. sun

## What Are Elements? (page 87)

1. T
2. T
3. T
4. F
5. T
6. F
7. T
8. T
9. F
10. T

## Structure of Atoms (page 88)

1. E
2. F
3. B
4. A
5. C
6. D
7. G

## Molecules (page 89)

1. compound
2. solid
3. oxygen
4. liquid
5. atoms
6. gas
7. molecules
8. temperature

## Periodic Table (page 90)

1. symbol
2. elements
3. number
4. weight
5. group, properties
6. period

## Chemical Formulas (page 91)

1. hydrogen, oxygen
2. 12, 22, 11
3. 45
4. four
5. six
6. four
7. three

## Changes of State (page 92)

1. temperature
2. solid, liquid
3. water
4. carbon dioxide, gas
5. gas
6. liquid

## Density of Matter (page 93)

Answers will vary somewhat but must include the idea that the paper clip has a greater density and tell why. Its molecules are more crowded. This makes it heavy for its size, even though it doesn't feel heavy and is small. The ocean liner takes up a tremendous volume, so it is not too heavy for its size to float. It has a lower density.

## Physical Properties of Matter (page 94)

Put a ✔ by 1, 2, 3, 5, 6, 8, and 10.

## Metals vs. Nonmetals (page 95)

1. M
2. N
3. M
4. M
5. M
6. N
7. M
8. N
9. M
10. N

## Dissolving in Water (page 96)

1. T
2. T
3. F
4. T
5. F
6. T
7. T
8. F
9. T
10. T

## Solutions and Suspensions (page 97)

1. S
2. P
3. P
4. P
5. B
6. P
7. B
8. S
9. S
10. P

## Mixtures vs. Compounds (page 98)

**Mixtures:** made of compounds, elements, or both; not chemically combined; parts can be separated by physical means; retains original properties; cannot write a formula
**Compounds:** made up of elements; chemically combined; parts cannot be easily separated; has new and different properties; has a formula

## Chemical Properties of Matter (page 99)

Put a ✔ by 1, 2, 4, 5, 6, 8, and 9.

## Chemical Changes (page 100)

1. C
2. R
3. D
4. C
5. D
6. R
7. R

## Physical or Chemical Change? (page 101)

1. P
2. C
3. P
4. P
5. P
6. C
7. C
8. P
9. P
10. C

## Chemistry Word Scramble (page 102)

1. element
2. molecule
3. compound
4. properties
5. atom
6. matter
7. chemistry
8. solution
9. nucleus
10. electrons

## Heat Energy (page 103)

1. warmer, colder
2. evaporate
3. freeze
4. melt
5. lead
6. candle wax
7. iron

## Sources of Heat (page 104)

1. B
2. E
3. F
4. G
5. C
6. A
7. D

## Heat Conduction (page 105)

1. F
2. T
3. F
4. T
5. T
6. T
7. F
8. T

## Heat Conductors and Insulators (page 106)

**Conductors:** copper, silver, iron, aluminum, and brass
**Insulators:** wood, Styrofoam, paper, wool, and cork

## Expansion and Contraction (page 107)

1. T
2. T
3. F
4. T
5. F
6. T
7. T
8. F
9. T
10. T

## Convection and Radiation (page 108)

1. sun
2. convection
3. wind, ocean, molecules
4. radiate
5. outer space
6. within

## Electromagnetic Spectrum (page 109)

1. T
2. F
3. T
4. T
5. F
6. T
7. T
8. F
9. T
10. T

## Infrared and Microwaves (page 110)

1. energy
2. warm
3. glow
4. invisible
5. food
6. molecules
7. heat
8. metal

## Sunlight and Blue Sky (page 111)

1. F
2. T
3. T
4. T
5. F
6. T
7. T
8. T
9. F
10. F

## Ultraviolet Light (page 112)

1. invisible
2. butterflies
3. sunburn
4. wrinkles, cancer
5. window
6. disinfect
7. black

## Fiber Optics (page 113)

1. T
2. T
3. F
4. T
5. F
6. T
7. T
8. T
9. F
10. T

## Lasers (page 114)

Put a ✓ by 2, 3, 4, 5, 7, and 10.